of daughters I
think you too,
will find beauty
in Allisons
journey.

Fain

Porcelain Angel

A daughter's journal of a mother's journey through multiple sclerosis

Allison Redfern

To the Reader:
The nonitalicized words are my reflections, thoughts, and memories.

The italicized words, with dates, are journal entries.
No words, grammar, or punctuation have been altered.
[Brackets in the journal entries are for clarification purposes only]

Poems are identified by indentation.
The date the poem was written, if known, is noted.

My heart and soul revealed—Allison

PORCELAIN ANGEL

Porcelain Angel
Matting Leah Publishing Company/February 2013

Published by Matting Leah Publishing Company
Warwick, New York.

Printed in China

Book Design by Tom Lennon

Cataloging-in-Publication Data

Redfern, Allison

Porcelain Angel: a daughter's journal of a mother's journey through
multiple sclerosis / Allison Redfern. --Warwick, NY: Matting Leah Pub. Co., c2012
   p. ; cm.
   ISBN: 978-0-9761528-4-2;
   Summary: The author's excerpted diary, beginning in early childhood, chronicling her
   mother's diagnosis and subsequent battle with MS, as well as the practical and emotional
   impact that diagnosis had on the author and her family.--Publisher

   1. Redfern, Jane Rolston. 2. Multiple sclerosis--Patients--Biography. 3. Mother's--death--
   Psychological aspects. I. Title.
RC377 .R43 2012
362.1968/340092--23   1210.

This book is dedicated to my mother and father,
whose relationship was a constant example of how to love.

Porcelain Angel

"We've had an expiration." Then, with a slight chuckle, the nurse added, "Don't worry, it's not your wife." I stood next to my father and tried to glance at his expression. We were hovering in the neurology corridor of Barnes Hospital in St. Louis, Missouri, and, evidently, this was the ICU nurse's way of telling us that visiting hours were being delayed. *An expiration.* I doubt I'll ever forget a death being described that way. I felt paralyzed in an awkward stance and didn't turn to see my younger sister's reaction. To this day, twenty-four years later, we've never discussed that moment.

It was Christmas Day, 1987. I was a junior in college and my sister, Carolyn, almost three years younger, a high school senior. Our mother was lying in That Room. Our father held a porcelain angel tightly in his grasp to place by her bedside, whenever we were allowed in The Room. Her body was adorned with needles, tubes, and surgical tape. She wouldn't recognize our faces even if she willed her eyelids to unfold. The daughters she had cradled and nourished, the daughters she taught to read and pray, the daughters she kept fighting to stay in this world for . . . girls who would now appear as strangers in a muddled world of life-support machines, beeping endlessly for attention. But maybe, just maybe she could distinguish a voice. Not just a familiar voice you overhear ordering dinner at the table next to you, but a voice from your soul. This voice resonates, because, though it may not have spoken the most profound words to have fallen upon your ears, this voice has uttered the phrases that make life worth living . . . the voice that has said, "More bubbles in the tub, Mommy . . . can I go play outside Mom? . . . Mom, I've decided on a college." So perhaps, she would wake and know our *voices.* I was always hoping for a miracle. We had been here before—many times over a number of years. But this time, this year, seemed far more grave. But my mother didn't die.

Your mother is the one person who has been with you from the very beginning. She is the root entwined through the rest of your life. She is the person you either want to emulate or the person you hope to never become. For most of us, our mother's character has determined our own by threading herself through our decisions and dreams. Even as I feverishly reached beyond the comfort of my mother's warm embrace, searching for my independence, she dug the root in deeper so that I would always feel its presence steadying my life. When my mother became ill, the branches of my existence were forever altered. Your social outlook, the way you view the world and relate to others, is different once you watch someone live through pain and suffering. But it wasn't all pain and suffering. Despite it all, I think my mother would say she had a wonderful life.

Us

My mother and father, Jane and Rex, met soon after high school. They were both raised in small, rural, mostly farming communities in western Illinois. They married their junior year of college, in 1956, and after graduation both became teachers. Several years passed and my father secured a job as an accountant and eventually became a CPA with a firm in St. Louis, Missouri. My older sister, Diana, was born in 1958. I finally arrived in 1967. My younger sister, Carolyn, came along in 1969. My sisters and I have a unique relationship. When Carolyn and I were young, Diana was often our babysitter and enjoyed dressing us up in vintage clothing and our mother's old wigs. Diana is nine years older than I am and eleven years older than Carolyn, so when I was nine, Diana went off to college. She married when I was thirteen. Unfortunately, I have only fleeting memories of Diana living in our home. As we grew older, however, the age gap diminished and today my sisters are my best friends.

My mother was one of five children, though her sister, JoAnn, died at age six of leukemia. My mother grew up in a very loving, spiritual home and was a musician at heart. She practiced diligently and was apparently quite accomplished as a pianist in her small Illinois town of Franklin. She also had two sisters, and they maintained a friendship with one another throughout their lives. After marrying, my mother spent the 1960s raising my older sister and me. She was a mother and housewife and seemed fulfilled in those identities. My mother grooved into the 1970s as a walking cliché! She wore the beehive hairdo, go-go boots, and printed scarves. She baked casseroles, served fondue, and attended bridge club. She dabbled in ceramics, sewed her own clothes, and played piano. She volunteered as a Girl Scout leader and room mother at my elementary school. She wrote poetry, arranged neighborhood "gourmet clubs," and participated in a weekly Bible study. The women involved in the study often teased that as long as an open Bible lay on the table among them, they could discuss local gossip and still call themselves a "Bible study group."

My father had one brother and was also reared in a small Illinois town, Palmyra. His parents were loving but not particularly affectionate. My father played basketball, football, and baseball and sang in the school choir. He joked that this was a result of the limited enrollment at his high school; every boy participated in all of the activities. If you ever hear my father sing, you would find this statement to be accurate . . . a warm body was apparently the only prerequisite for choir participation. After my parents married and moved to St. Louis, my father went to work every day crunching numbers. When he eventually retired from his accounting firm thirty plus years later, someone told me he had taken only a handful of sick days his entire career. (Presumably those were the days he was hospitalized after his appendix ruptured!) My father is an avid gardener, enjoys golf (well, sometimes *enjoys* golf), and always wins in gin rummy and Scrabble.

I don't recall experiencing anger in our home. I'm quite sure my parents argued, but I didn't witness these episodes. Some may not believe this but at age forty-five, I have never heard my father raise his voice. What a gift to give a child. Though we were middle class, we enjoyed family vacations throughout the United States. My grandparents, who visited every state, raised my parents to seize the notion that you will eventually make the money to pay the bills, but if you wait until you're old and established to travel, it will be too late.

As a young girl, Diana was a Girl Scout and gymnast, but her passion was art, which continues to blossom. She is extremely talented as an artist but often doesn't acknowledge her gift, because for her, it comes so easily. She became a mother and gave her life to her daughters and husband. Family, home, and tradition became her passions. Carolyn was a gymnast, track star, and swimmer. She held a swim club record in the breast stroke for years. She excelled in math as a student but eventually she earned her way into law school and became an attorney, and then a mother. And me, well, I was a dancer, a gymnast, and quite a dreamer. What became of me? Read on . . .

My childhood was idyllic. I wasn't even too aware that the childhoods of others may not mimic mine. Now that I'm older and work in a field where I investigate the horrors of how people live and treat children, I realize my friends or neighbors were probably experiencing lives I could not imagine. But mine . . . mine was carefree and easy, and I seemed to want for nothing. Lying just beneath the surface of that perfect life, however, was multiple sclerosis.

Multiple Sclerosis

Every hour in the United States, someone is newly diagnosed with multiple sclerosis, an unpredictable, often disabling disease of the central nervous system.

Multiple sclerosis, or MS, is a disease that affects the brain and spinal cord, resulting in loss of muscle control, vision, balance, and sensation (such as numbness). With MS, the nerves of the brain and spinal cord are damaged by one's own immune system. Thus, the condition is called an autoimmune disease.

The most common early symptoms of MS include:

- Tingling
- Numbness
- Loss of balance
- Weakness in one or more limbs
- Blurred or double vision

MS usually strikes adults in the prime of life—between the ages of twenty and forty.

75 percent of people with MS are women.

MS affects more than 400,000 in the United States and 2.5 million worldwide.

The Journals

My mother later explained to me that she would be lying in bed and feel like her fingers were numb or sharp pains would shoot through her limbs. She experienced excruciating discomfort in her back and sometimes she would stumble like her equilibrium was off. She initially visited several physicians without receiving a diagnosis, and then she began researching her symptoms. In the early 1970s, multiple sclerosis was not commonly diagnosed and many were unfamiliar with the signs and symptoms of the disease. A neurologist finally confirmed my mother's fears. I say fears, because there were not treatments for MS then that there are today. My mother was thirty-seven years old, had three daughters, two under the age of six, and she feared for her future, their future, if the disease or her condition worsened. I could not have known the gravity of the news. I was only five. I was dressing Barbies and instructing Carolyn how to shovel sand in our boxed-in beach. How did my parents react? Did they discuss the prognosis? There likely was not one. Did they pretend it wasn't happening and all would be well? Looking back, I question why I never asked my mother, "What was that like? Were you scared?"

Though I do have her journals . . . I became a journal writer at an early age, probably because I watched my mother keeping a diary. My early "journals" were small diaries with a lock and key attached. The key had to be hidden in a clandestine compartment under my socks and panties, because what if someone managed to break in and read the intimate details of my life as a sixth grader? My secrets would be revealed! I had certainly contemplated the implications of noting into history that school had been canceled due to snow, or that I had eaten a Hostess Ding Dong and watched *Charlie's Angels*. Hadn't I? And those really are the occurrences I felt should be recorded . . . my after-school snack and the television programs I watched that evening. There was the occasional life-altering event, such as "I got my first bra," but for the most part, I can return to my childhood days to reflect on the Twinkies.

ALLISON—March 7, 1978: Today Carolyn and I both stayed home from school. Tonight we watched Happy Days.

ALLISON—March 8, 1978: Today was like yesterday, except we watched Charlie's Angels and Starsky and Hutch.

So, while I was making note of which NBC program was molding my young mind, my mother was putting her life into words.

1968

(My mother is thirty-three and I am one)

JANE—March 18, 1968: My back hurt so bad all day—got an appt. at doc for tomorrow night.

JANE—March 19, 1968: Went to the doc tonight. He couldn't decide what was wrong—says I'm not pregnant but my back hurts so bad, it's just an orthopedic problem.

JANE—March 26, 1968: went to Bridge club, really enjoyed it but my back hurt awfully bad

JANE—June 3, 1968: Our 12th anniversary! Rex brought me a 3 pound box of Mavrakos chocolates.

JANE—September 18, 1968: Edna kept Allison while I went to the doc. Got a hormone shot. He says I'm pregnant for sure but may have trouble.

JANE—September 21, 1968: Been having cramps so called the doc. Said it didn't look good. Diana and Rex are disappointed, so am I—but so thankful it was this time instead of last. Felt bad all evening, couldn't go to sleep.

JANE—September 22, 1968: Rex helped me—fixed a big breakfast then a big dinner. Late this evening I guess I really had the miscarriage. It really shook me up, just wonder if it was a boy or girl.

After Diana was born, my mother waited nine years for my arrival. As Diana blew the candles on her cake each September, my mother and father longed for her to have a sibling. My mother suppressed her disappointment each month, as infertility was not something couples discussed in those days. However, I'm not sure how diligent my parents were in their endeavors to conceive. I doubt my mother knew how to calculate her "cycle." Ovulation was not common terminology, and so I suspect my parents' attempts were mere shots in the dark.

I know very little of my mother's astonishment when she finally learned in 1966 that she was "expecting." On March 27, 1967, my parents went to the cinema, munched on popped corn and snuggled in to watch *Dr. Zhivago.* During the Russian tryst, my mother was transported into labor and gave birth to me the following day. According to these journal entries, she miscarried the next year, in 1968. Our family became complete when my dear sister Carolyn joined us in 1969.

Why God Made Little Girls
[author unknown]

God made the world with its towering trees, majestic mountains and restless seas,
Then he paused and said, "It needs one more thing,
Someone to laugh and dance and sing,
To walk in the woods and gather flowers,
To commune with nature in quiet hours,"
So God created little girls, with laughing eyes and bouncing curls,
With joyful hearts and infectious smiles,
Enchanting ways and feminine wiles.
And when He'd completed the task He'd begun,
He was pleased and proud of the job He'd done,
For the world when seen through a little girl's eyes,
Greatly resembles paradise.

This poem proudly hung in the spare bedroom of our home throughout my childhood. On occasion I would sneak into the guest quarters as though through a secret trap door. The small room, with its pale-blue walls, was an oasis where I could snuggle under the fluffy white duvet and daydream of worlds beyond my own. As I lay in the bed, my eyes often fell upon the "Little Girls" rhyme, plastered to a wooden plaque. The poem was a constant reminder that no matter which paths we each chose in the woods, our parents would always treasure their three little girls.

1972

(My mother is thirty-seven and I am five)

JANE—January 28, 1972: Rex drove me to doc Mendelsohn—Diana stayed home to babysit. I get so <u>mad</u>. I know <u>something</u> causes my feet and legs to act so crazy but no one can seem to find the trouble. I <u>am</u> <u>not</u> going back to him <u>ever.</u> Guess I'll try to improve my diet and exercise. Took Allison and Carolyn to see "Disney on Parade." They were so excited. Allison really enjoyed it, especially the "Sleeping Beauty" part. Carolyn was good but sleepy.

JANE—February 9, 1972: My birthday! Good ole Diana—she had breakfast ready when I got up—candle in a roll. Went shopping for 1 ½ hours, just to look around. When I got home the girls had decorated the kitchen and baked a cake.

JANE—February 18, 1972: Diana went to 8th grade party—she likes a 9th grade boy now—I don't like that too well.

JANE—March 8, 1972: Went to Dr. Reynolds (orthopedic surgeon), he said I should try a neurologist??? That's what Dr. Mendelsohn is—I give up!

JANE—March 17, 1972: Went back to Mendelsohn today. I never would have gone to him again except Rex called him. Honestly—I'll never understand doctors. He acted like I should have known all along that it is MS. I just don't know. I think I could stand most anything except if I'd lose my eyesight. What would be the use of anything then. Rex was so understanding. God—I could not stand it without him. My biggest worry is how can I expect him to sit around with a cripple the rest of his life. Also, the girls—

JANE—June 29, 1972: Rex made partner! He called around 11, wanted to know what I was doing—talked for a while then said, "I made it." Uncorked a bottle of champagne this evening!

JANE—July 3, 1972: We all went to my doc at 3:00. First visit to Doctor Berg. He seems very nice—no new ideas, though thinks it is MS.

JANE—July 5, 1972: Not much to do today, cleaned house, washed, ironed. Rex got groceries for me. Sure hate that but can hardly take both girls and get all that stuff. Legs get so tired.

JANE—July 7, 1972: Rex had planned to take the day off but ended up working til noon—came home and he and I played golf at Norwood. Ate lunch there too. Such a beautiful day—cool—I get so tired though, could only play 8 holes then rode in the cart while Rex played. Charcoaled hamburgers. I always hate to leave the girls for so long.

JANE—July 11, 1972: I just don't feel like I spend enough time doing things with A&C. They play outside so much. I don't want them to grow up so fast.

JANE—July 21, 1972: Leave for French Lick, Indiana, arrive 2:30! Swim, surrey ride, dinner at 6:30. Kids! I always want to take them but they are still awfully young. They get so tired waiting to eat. They were real good in the dining room. Carolyn wet her pants. I wiped it up with a linen napkin. The waiter came by and tied the napkin around her neck so she could eat spaghetti. We about cracked up.

JANE—August 1, 1972: Allison and Carolyn talking in bathroom about the bubbles in the tub. Allison said, "gosh I wish you were bigger you're so dumb."

JANE—August 4, 1972: Diana practically threw a fit when we wouldn't let her go see "The Graduate." She apologized but sure got upset with us.

JANE—August 31, 1972: First day of school! Allison was so anxious to go. She is really ready for it, Carolyn cried when she left.

JANE—October 24, 1972: Went to Monte Carlo party on the Robert E. Lee for the Multiple Sclerosis Society.

JANE—December 5, 1972: Read 'Night Before Christmas' to the girls —Allison seems to just believe it all with no questions. Carolyn said when I finished, "I think only birds can fly."

JANE—December 9, 1972: Took the girls downtown to see decorations and talk to Santa. Famous Barr used a Raggedy Ann theme, so cute. The girls sat on Santa's lap—Carolyn didn't talk but Allison told him a couple of things she wanted. We ate at Famous. A real fun day except my poor legs just won't hold up for more than an hour?? Makes me worry—

JANE—December 15, 1972: [Ernst & Ernst CPA] firm party tonight—enjoyed it except Charlie Blank asked me to dance and I did—reluctantly—I was so worried I would fall, etc.

1973

(My mother is thirty-eight and I am six)

JANE—February 9, 1973: [Mom's birthday] When I woke up Diana was busy cooking breakfast—she is so thoughtful. Betty had 3 neighbors & myself for lunch for me—They even all brought <u>gifts</u>. We all went to Flaming Pit for supper.

JANE—March, 21 1973: Got our new station wagon! Girls were so excited

JANE—March 22, 1973: A&C up at 7:00 am to sit in new car. Went to Dr. Stafford (ophthalmologist) Have been having trouble seeing for past several months—Just what I've been so afraid of—a blind spot on the left cornea—caused by M.S. Put me on cortisone—16 pills at once—What will I do if this doesn't improve? Rex is always so optimistic.

JANE—March 25, 1973: A lovely <u>fun</u> day. Went to church then to Stouffers downtown for brunch—took folks to top of the Arch.

JANE—March 28, 1973: Birthday party for Allison—17 kids what a mess! Allison really enjoyed it and I like to have parties for them but this one was wild! <u>Too</u> many kids

JANE—April 1, 1973: A&C & I baked apple pies, popped corn, built a fire. Very relaxing and enjoyable day!

JANE—April 19, 1973: Rain! as usual! Baked a coffee cake. Watched "The Waltons Easter Story"—very good—the mother had polio and they kept telling her she'd have to be in a wheelchair. She didn't give up trying and learned to walk again.

JANE—April 22, 1973: Hunt Easter baskets! Allison was up at 5:45. She gets so excited. Went to church 9:30 we were greeters. Brunch on the deck, our <u>new</u> furniture. It was <u>so</u> beautiful eating out there. Layed in sun, worked in yard. Made homemade ice cream

Hunting for pastel-colored baskets and dyed eggs in the dew-stained grass was an annual Easter tradition. The weather in St. Louis was often cool and damp as pink tulips and yellow daffodils blossomed in the flower beds. Carolyn and I welcomed the holiday dressed alike, with our shining black patent-leather shoes, white knee socks, homemade Easter dresses, and spring coats. Our family attended Easter church services, as my sister and I tightly cradled a new stuffed bunny or lamb.

JANE—April 23, 1973: Eye doc at 8:15, Rex took me and kept girls in the car. It still isn't much better—He said it may take a long time to improve.

JANE—May 11, 1973: What a busy day! Ran errands this am. Edna and I had lunch at Famous, she drove me to Dr. Berg's. He said to see if the MS gets worse in next few mo—if it does—go to the hosp for 10 days for injections of ACTH?

Edna and my mother became friends in the early 1960s when, as neighbors, they swapped sugar and oleo. They maintained a lifelong friendship that progressed from recipe exchange, to gossiping over bottomless cups of coffee, babysitting each other's children, and, eventually, a caretaking most friends are not accustomed to. When Edna's finances were suffering, my mother suggested she clean homes for neighbors. Edna was uncomfortable with this idea and so she "practiced" her skills on our home, with my mother's guidance and instruction. As MS waged its war and my mother's legs grew weaker, Edna became our weekly housekeeper. I'm not sure how much of Edna's time was spent scrubbing floors or how much was devoted to her favorite pastime, talking. Edna had the gift of gab. She could chat for hours, as was often the case when she and my mother connected by phone. I laugh when I recall my mother shackled to the telephone, with Edna on the other end of the line. It was the era when telephones were married to the wall, when one could only travel the distance the cord would extend. There is probably little they didn't discuss. I often wonder what it was like for Edna, to watch her friend's health slowly deteriorate through the years.

JANE—October 31, 1973: Halloween party at the barn—then took girls Trick or Treating. They sure had fun and so much candy—they dressed as clowns. Diana went to a party—dressed as a little girl.

JANE—November 2, 1973: Tawny is in heat, I sure wish she'd get pregnant. I'd love for her to have pups but can't seem to sneak her out without Rex knowing. I let her out twice but he discovered it too soon and called her in!!

Tawny was our lovely golden retriever that Santa had delivered one year complete with a bright-red bow draped around her furry neck. She was our first pet, and though my memories seem to focus on her running wild through our neighborhood, she helped develop a degree of "dog love" for me. This journal entry of my mother's, attempting to impregnate Tawny, makes me laugh. My mother (well, Tawny) was successful. Sometime later, Tawny met her mate. She birthed her litter on our concrete floor garage, my mother, sleeves rolled up, assisting with each new pup. Two died, events that seemed to border on hysterical for me. I wanted to keep the entire family. Alas, these pups were for sale, and though I was a young child, I wondered if Tawny thought this a good business venture. Should a mother ever have to separate from her offspring?

1976

(My mother is forty-one and I am nine)

ALLISON—February 9, 1976: I went to gymnastics. Today was moms birthday and she got some nice gifts. [One of my first, riveting journal entries].

ALLISON—February 14, 1976 [Valentine's Day]: I watched a children's film on TV. And I had diving lessons. And when dad got home from work he got me a box of candy. Mom got me a plant and a card.

As the story goes, when my parents were dating and the calendar presented their first Valentine's Day together, my mother's friends were receiving cards, flowers, and candy. My mother received nothing. In his defense, my father was raised by two conservative individuals and he had only a brother. No girls, no frills, no hearts or love songs in the home. After enduring my mother's wrath and tears at his lack of playing Cupid, he never forgot another Valentine's Day. Every February 14 my father arrived home from work, clutching pink or ruby-colored heart-shaped boxes of chocolates for each of his girls.

ALLISON—February 19, 1976: After school I had piano and my piano teacher didn't give me any new peaces [pieces]. I got sad and I want to quit and I want to take piano from my mom.

ALLISON—March 10, 1976: Carolyn went to a birthday party and I had a ding dong while she was gone.

ALLISON—April 3, 1976: Mom went to Minnesota with Grandma Rolston to the Male Clienic [Mayo Clinic] to see if they could help her legs.

ALLISON—April 10, 1976: Mom came home from Minnesota and I was glad. They couldn't help her legs. Mom brought me and Carolyn a little stuffed animal and some lipstick.

When I was young and my mother was able, she was the mother most dream of having. Arriving home from school, Rice Krispies Treats awaited us. Puffed-rice cereal mixed with that gooey combination of marshmallows and butter, chilled to perfection. I would burst through the front door to that familiar smell of home. The one you can't quite describe but just know, if you ever smell it again. Drop off the book bag and head straight to the refrigerator to see the long, scuffed metal pan of homemade treats beckoning my sister and me. Beside it there might also have been a strawberry Jell-O mold resting for that night's dinner.

We lived in a suburb of St. Louis County, Missouri, at the base of a hill where two streets converged. Modest homes lined the streets, and our neighborhood was clouded with school-age children. Because of the particular location of our home, we were the epicenter for after-school play or summer-evening activities: four square, capture the flag, kickball, Red Rover. On Halloween the sidewalks were flooded with petite masqueraders. The homes were situated close enough so that maximum candy hoarding was possible. You could quickly make your way from neighbor to neighbor, increasing your loot in a small span of time. Behind our home was a small, rocky creek that stretched for what seemed like miles when I was a child. I loved playing in the creek as did many of the neighborhood children. Though when I dabbled in the creek bed, I imagined myself as Pippi Longstocking. I had seen a movie or television program featuring the red-braided orphan and, oh, how I longed to be her! She was always searching for clues, discovering trinkets, and solving mysteries.

ALLISON—March 7, 1976: Me and Carolyn played by the creek. We got rocks and threw them in the creek and we dug mud and touched the water with sticks. And we played [Fisher Price] People in the sand.

Years later, during a difficult time in my life, I was reminiscing about "my creek" and jotted down this poem:

[Allison] 1995: <u>The Creek at 455</u>
I used to sit among the rocks, and dream of what would be
I was off on an adventure, I'd pretend I wasn't me.
The water seeping through my toes, was always cold at first
But as a child I didn't mind, my creek was well rehearsed.
The trees that towered overhead, threw shade upon my world
At times I'd climb them to the top, all when I was just a girl.
The creek is small and narrow now, the trees are not so tall

Allison Redfern

Will I step into the water, or do I fear the fall?
Why don't I take chances now, I used to be so bold
Free and fearless is a child's heart, Mine is growing old.

1977

(My mother is forty-two and I am ten)

Carolyn and I were members of the Cool Dell swim team for several years. We both swam and I also dove. I coveted diving lessons but recall dreading swim practice. My mother would wake us each summer morning so we could greet the dawn and head to the mystical waters of a pool that seemed to have no end. I doubt it was dawn, but when I was a young child, on a break from elementary school, the waking hour seemed excruciatingly early. We would stumble out of bed, slip into our green and white Speedos, and shuffle out to the street curb, waiting for our carpool ride. The coach's whistle blared as we completed each lap, signaling that rest was not on the horizon. The best aspect of swim team was the meets. Cool Dell would face off against another swim club for an hours-long battle. Parents cheered on their miniature human dolphins, racing for a blue, red, or white ribbon. The day of the meet was a "rest day"—no practice! Swimmers were instructed to relax and mentally prepare for the evening challenge. At ages ten and seven, Carolyn and I were likely not capable of mentally preparing for anything, but we certainly took advantage of the rest day. We were confined to our bedroom, playing Monopoly and scripting childhood plays. It amuses me now, as though we were resting our muscles, preserving our energy for an Olympic time trial.

Each holiday summoned tattered cardboard boxes from the basement, filled with decorations for our home. Most were ceramic items or something sewn by my mother. Others were gifts from friends or relatives, and many were trinkets handmade by my sisters or me. There were hearts and doilies for Valentine's Day; a green ceramic basket filled with delicately painted ceramic eggs resting in pastel colored Easter grass for the April holiday; miniature American flags and red, white, and blue candles in July; and autumn presented the ceramic pumpkin whose lid could be removed to reveal Snickers, Reeses and Milky Way bars. At Christmas, however, our home was transformed into a winter wonderland display, as it seemed that each corner of every room held holiday garland. Every December our family would pile into the family car and travel to the neighborhood Lion's Club tree lot, where my parents selected their favorite Douglas fir. My mother also had a white artificial tree. "Artificial" was nearly a dirty word in our home at Christmas, though, for the white tree, it could be uttered. This tree stood proudly in the living room, among the pale-blue shag carpeting and white sofa. The white tree was adorned with royal-blue balls and bows, silver tinsel, and strings of blue and white lights. It was quite regal and pristine, like a snow-covered pine tree in the woods. Adjacent to the white tree sat my mother's piano. As she played and sang carols, Carolyn and I danced around the white tree as if we were fairies in the forest, in footie pajamas.

1978

(My mother is forty-three and I am eleven)

ALLISON—January 15, 1978: Today I went sledding. Our family watched the Superbowl. Dallas vs. Denver. Dallas won! Hurray

I suppose in my child's mind I feared that my father had wanted a boy the second time around and I had been a disappointment. I played T-ball and tried to emulate a "tomboy," though my father later told me that at the end of the T-ball games, I usually asked, "Who won?" I also learned the mascot for each NFL football team, again, in the hopes of impressing my father with my sports knowledge. As an adult, and knowing the father I have, he was happy with me just the way I was.

ALLISON—January 25, 1978: Today we didn't have school. It snowed 7 to 10 inches. Last night I made Valentines, I wish I had a boyfriend.

ALLISON—February 2, 1978: I don't have a boyfriend and I've got to find one!

ALLISON—February 8, 1978: Carolyn and I bought mom a watch for her birthday, it is tomorrow. The watch was $20

My mother wore the silver-plated watch for years, every day. My sister and I had purchased it from Target, but she wore it like it was from Tiffany's.

ALLISON—February 19, 1978: Today our family went looking for houses. I don't want to move. Tonight we watched Hardy Boys.

ALLISON—February 27, 1978: After school mom told me about my period some more. And about having children when I get older.

I vaguely remember my mother having the "birds and the bees" conversation with me. I was summoned into her bedroom, and we sat eye to eye, two women of the world. This appeared to be a serious topic. Was I the bird or the bee? A woman who lived down the street was pregnant, and after my mother generally described "the deed," I was almost sick to my stomach that this woman and her husband had done *that*. They hardly seemed to like each other!

ALLISON—April 2, 1978: Today dad told me we are going to move. He bought a house today. We are moving in September.

By October 1978, our new home in Chesterfield, Missouri had been built roughly ten miles west of where my sisters and I had grown up. Though the architect's plans allowed Carolyn and me to "choose" and decorate our own bedrooms, we would also be enrolling in a new school. I was both ecstatic and nervous about this migration. In November, before the move had actually occurred, my sisters, parents, and I snuck into our new home, built a fire, and slept on the living room floor in sleeping bags. We made s'mores over the hot, snapping fire; crisp graham crackers, smothered with a chocolate Hershey bar and melted marshmallows. This might not be so bad after all.

For the month of December each year, my mother always encouraged my sisters and me to open an advent calendar. Though I was meant to be appreciating the religious significance of the advent season, I secretly anticipated each year's calendar, wondering which window I would get to open, revealing a yuletide delight. Usually the advent calendar windows opened to a line from a favorite Christmas carol or a picture of a holiday ornament. But on occasion my mother would treat us to a calendar that held a rich chocolate for each day of December. One year our advent calendar was even more special than chocolates (who would of thought that were possible!) On each day of December, Carolyn or I would get to open a small gift. Each present was wrapped in colorful red or green shiny paper, and tucked inside was an addition for our dollhouse. During the month of December the year prior, my father had arrived home from work and then retired to the basement, where he spent his evenings constructing a three-story dollhouse, with two delicate stairwells, tediously placed shingles, and a wrap-around front porch. We had received the miniature mansion from Santa that year, and this Christmas, our advent "calendar" was a special way for my mother to add to our doll play. One day Carolyn would unwrap a new dining table and the next day I would open a crocheted rug for the bedroom. My mother had placed all twenty-five packages in a basket on the kitchen table, so as we woke each morning that December, we could choose which gift we wanted to open on "our day." The secret was to inspect the packages carefully in the hopes of revealing the best of the loot.

1979

(My mother is forty-four and I am twelve)

ALLISON—January 1, 1979: We took down our Christmas tree. We got a puppy for Christmas, its name is Pepper.

Pepper became my mother's beloved companion. He was a black mutt but a wonderful pet. Eventually, as Pepper grew older and seemed to understand my mother's condition, he could "fetch" my father. My mother would be lying in bed, and if she needed my father, who may be in the kitchen or family room, she would say with urgency, "Pepper, go get Rex!" Pepper would run to where my father was and bark, beckoning him to her bedside.

ALLISON —January 18, 1979: I did a back flip! By myself 5 times. This was one of the best days in my life!

Some children spend their adolescence on a baseball or soccer field, others on the tennis court, and many lounging in front of the television. I spent my evenings at the Dance Workshoppe. My mother enrolled each of us in dance at a very early age. Once I became a serious dance student, this activity consumed my time. The Dance Workshoppe was a small studio in St. Louis County. Upon arrival, pupils and parents were greeted by our teacher's mother, a chain smoker with a nice figure for an elderly woman. The front reception area housed a gallery of photographs from recitals past, with dancers costumed in sequins, tulle, and tights. Two steps down the hall sat a dressing room, always congested with ballerinas tying up pointe shoes and gossiping about their day's activities. Beyond that door was the studio portion, complete with a long ballet bar and mirrors on two adjacent walls. Our teacher, Estelle, had once been a ballerina but had let her body expand through years of inactivity. She was sometimes pleasant, often difficult, and rarely normal. I attended ballet on Mondays, jazz class on Tuesdays, pointe on Wednesdays, and gymnastics on Thursdays. Guess who was tasked with driving me to and from? I never appreciated that my parents' evenings were bombarded with my passion for dance. I have only fond memories of my years studying and feel the art transformed my life in numerous ways.

ALLISON—January 21, 1979: Today we watched the Superbowl! Cowboys vs. Steelers. Pittsburgh won, boo hoo!

ALLISON—January 30, 1979: Later today Carolyn was a brat. She said she knew where I hide my diary and that she had read it!

ALLISON—March 28, 1979: I got the chicken pox! [my 12th birthday]

ALLISON—March 30, 1979: We went to Florida!

As the Florida trip was obviously previously planned and fully booked, my outbreak of chicken pox was a very unfortunate and untimely event. The morning of our departure, my mother slathered my face with liquid makeup and had me wear a long-sleeved blouse on the airplane. I recall my father saying, "Don't worry, people will just think you have a bad case of acne." Exactly what a twelve-year-old girl wants people to think. We made the trip to Disneyworld, my skin covered with unsightly bumps. I wore a large-billed hat to cover my face; my mother feared that other park goers might be concerned that her child was spreading the chicken pox (which I likely was). On Easter Sunday, my sister, Carolyn, woke to malted chocolate eggs and skin covered in scarlet-colored pox. A vacation to remember.

In December 1979, my older sister, Diana, got engaged. Somehow we knew it was coming. She had been dating Steve for three years, and there was a bottle of champagne chilling in the refrigerator on Christmas Eve. That night, as Diana and Steve sat in the "pit" (this was an area of our home adjacent to the fireplace but two steps lower than the family room. The fireplace opened to the pit on one side and the family room on the other), Carolyn and I crouched in the family room, peering through the fireplace at the "proposal." They hugged and kissed and as Diana stood, Carolyn and I quickly bolted back to our bedrooms and waited. Once Mom and Dad were told the good news, we all joined in the family room, where they enjoyed the champagne! My first bridesmaid experience now loomed on the horizon!

1980

(My mother is forty-five and I am thirteen)

JANE—January 8, 1980: This will certainly be a year to remember. We just had the most wonderful Christmas. Everyone was so happy—Diana getting her ring.

JANE—January 24, 1980: spent this week making Allison's bridesmaid dress! 2 will be enough to make—Ha. I'm so anxious for Diana to see it—afraid it isn't what she had in mind! Wish I could teach all 3 girls to have more patience!

JANE—February 2, 1980: Took A&C to Castle Oak for gymnastics. Diana and I shopped. I really did good, felt good and enjoyed it. I've been walking around the basement several times each night. Hope it helps my back.

JANE—February 9, 1980: [my mother's birthday] Ali brought me breakfast in bed (fruit, omelet, real good). She just learned how to do an omelet in Home Ec. She is growing up so much—really a big help to me.

JANE—February 10, 1980: I really feel poopy. I keep wondering how I'm going to manage. Here I am, 45—I can't do a damn thing!

JANE—February 12, 1980: Had neighbors for a coffee—can't believe the get-together turned out good. Just 4 new neighbors but they all seemed so happy to come. Boy did I have trouble tho—could hardly get to the door etc. I must find something to make me feel like a useful and helpful person. I need to start here at home, cook better meals, etc.

JANE—February 13, 1980: Watched Donahue—hypnotism—wonder if that could help me. I'm going to try a form of self healing and see what happens. I'm so disgusted—I rested—took it easy all day and my back was horrible tonight! All I do is complain about my back!

JANE—February 14, 1980 [Valentine's Day]: Took Girl Scouts to visit their adopted Grandma and Grandpa at the nursing home. Pitiful there. I'd rather die than ever be in one. We went to Dairy Queen for treats. Rex brought us 3 candy. We are so lucky.

JANE—February 16, 1980: Went to Schmidts for dinner—I like that group <u>but</u> don't feel like I really belong. They ski, golf, tennis etc.

JANE—February 23, 1980: The Olympics have been so great to watch. I almost cry when I see those athletes who have worked so hard and do such a fantastic job. Everyone is so proud of the hockey team, young kids & beat Russia. What a thrill and Eric Heiden—5 gold medals!!

JANE—February 29, 1980: Went to see Dr. Trotter at Barnes. He thinks I may have a pinched nerve. Prescribed 3 valium, 5 mg a day for 5 days. See how I feel then.

JANE—March 1, 1980: Wow! Do I feel wobbly—legs and feet so numb like— back hurts less tho

JANE—March 2, 1980: didn't go to church, my back <u>so</u> stiff I could cry. Loosens up after I'm up.

JANE—March 3, 1980: back stiff but not bad pain—I did drive today, legs so weak.

JANE—March 16, 1980: Rex and Steve watched TV <u>all day.</u> They went to the Multiple Sclerosis banquet last night with us, really glad they did. Rex will be leaving his office of head of the MS Society. He has worked so hard on it and it took a lot of his time.

JANE—March 17, 1980: Snowing again—Just 2 & ½ weeks before Diana gets home again. Sure had a fun week with her, got a lot done—my dress, cake ordered, florist—Started the valium again today—½ pill 3 times. Felt good when I got up, for once.

JANE—March 20, 1980: What a shock—today Ali told me Kelly tried to get her to buy drugs at school, one of the times I was so thankful I was home so she could talk to me. She <u>wants</u> to do right—it is so difficult—all the pressure from kids.

JANE—March 23, 1980: church—Carolyn's piano recital at West County, her first time to play in public. She was a nervous wreck and so was I before, but she did it <u>perfectly.</u> Went for ice cream.

JANE—March 24 and 25, 1980: Felt awful—what <u>am</u> I going to do. The medication doesn't seem to help the back just makes my legs weak and me feel ikky.

JANE—March 28, 1980: [Allison's 13th birthday] Took Ali and Carolyn to see "Little Darlings" rated "R"—I must be nuts. I hope Carolyn didn't understand it. Ali wanted fried chicken for dinner. Gave her a phone. Diana sent her flowers — she <u>loved</u> getting them.

I remember going to see *Little Darlings*, but I don't think I really knew what the movie was about at the time (two girls attend summer camp and make a bet as to who will lose her virginity first). I imagine my mother wanted to crawl out of that theater with her thirteen and ten-year-olds! I cherished that phone. It was bright yellow and circular, like something from the *Mod Squad*. I was beyond cool. On our birthdays our mother let us choose our favorite dinner. I always selected fried chicken and mashed potatoes. My mother was an expert at frying a chicken. To this day I can taste that crisp, moist, delicious chicken when I close my eyes. As a young woman, I attempted this meal in my own kitchen. Disaster. The house smelled like grease for days, not to mention the chicken was quite pink on the inside.

JANE—April 9, 1980: Laid in bed—I lay on the couch and work on Diana's veil but at least I can work on that.

JANE—April 17, 1980: Back is better but I have to rest, I'm thankful—that seems to help, got a lot of jobs done today

JANE—May 4, 1980: Rex worked outside all day—I did some just <u>wished</u> I could last longer. Rex bought a wheelchair, took it to the nursery today. It is handy but I <u>hate</u> to have to use it.

JANE—May 9, 1980: Yea! Ali called and she made cheerleading—none of her close friends did. I got her a cake—said "Yea! Ali" They are really tough with the judging. She and I got pizza for dinner. Back was horrible!

JANE—May 11, 1980: Mothers Day. Nice day—went down on Riverfront—ate on floating McDonalds—took wheelchair—kids took skates. Diana called. Ali gave me a sun tea jar and heart sachet, Carolie went with a friend and got me a yellow mum plant all by herself. How lucky I am.

JANE—May 19, 1980: Thank goodness—a nice day, shopped in KC—looked around campus at KU. Took pictures—ate dinner—went to graduation at stadium. It was <u>beautiful</u>. So neat seeing them all march over the hill—4900 graduates. We were <u>so</u> proud of Diana.

JANE—May 23, 1980: Carolie's track meet! Diana and I watched from the hill (at Lafayette). She got 3rd in the 75 yard dash and 1st in running broad jump. This was the whole district!

JANE—June 25, 1980: [four days after Diana's wedding] What an absolutely <u>perfect</u> wedding it was. Everything went as planned and was beautiful. I was so touched by the presence of different people, people I never dreamed would come. What a wonderful day to remember. Diana looked so lovely—as did all the girls, the weather was perfect. Rex said, "if only we could wrap this day in a package and open it again sometime." He was so nervous before the ceremony—guess I was too but I couldn't say much—I just felt like sitting and watching—like it was all a dream.

JANE—July 7, 1980: Rex brought me to Barnes [Hospital] at 10:30—they took blood—did nothing all day. Got lunch at 4—took me to xray 9 to 10, 5 doctors examined me today, one at 11 to 12:30 at night

JANE—July 8, 1980: Took more blood—took me to do a CAT scan but machine broke—did nothing—Rex came about 12:00—He's going to take Ali to ballet then A&C to swim meet—They called at 10:15 to tell of the meet—We won— they did good.

JANE—July 9, 1980: Woke early—took a shower so I could be ready when they come to get me. At 8 I went to xray—did the chest again, also back—on to mylegram—not nearly so bad as I expected—have me sit up for 8 hrs (used to lay flat 8 yrs ago) Oh God! I pray they find something they can fix—Rex came at noon.

JANE—July 10, 1980: Well the worst is true—that sounds awful and ungrateful. They found nothing wrong in the xray or mylegram. It's so discouraging cause now I will go home the same way I came—today I went to PT then home

JANE—August 12, 1980: Dental appt—so hard for me, God! What am I going to do. I've been reading "Passages." I know I need something to get busy on—to learn or do—I can't just live as an extension of Rex and the girls—I tend to do that—If only I could walk!

Journal writing must have been a "release" for my mother, because our family rarely heard her complain or express concern about her condition. She was optimistic and approached her life and situation with a sense of humor.

JANE—August 21, 1980: Edna drove me to St. Charles to get hand controls on my car. I sure appreciated her taking me. The car is so much easier to drive. It is really neat.

What my mother's journal entry doesn't say is that her car was a Ford Pinto. As if Pintos weren't already unsafe. . .

ALLISON—1980: I start school in one day. I'm excited and nervous. I'll be in the 8th grade. I write like a 5th grader. I don't know if the kids will like me or not.

JANE—September 18, 1980: I went to Checkered Flag with Joan for a class. It wiped me out. Thank the Lord she was there to help me. I just couldn't move after it was over. Sat the whole time so I don't know what happened. My back has hurt so much this week. Talked to Dr. Trotter, I'm going to Jewish Hospital Pain Control Center (my idea)

I'm not sure of the exact year when my mother began using a cane, but I remember I didn't like it. *I* didn't like it. Did I mention I have always been selfish? I never asked my mother, but knowing her spirit and sense of determination, she hated it. The outward sign to the world that something is wrong, my body is failing me. Soon thereafter, my father bought her the wheelchair. When I was in the eighth grade, we had a pep assembly at school for the parents to attend. I was a cheerleader and would be performing. My mother told me she would probably have to attend in the wheelchair as the parking lot was a distance from the gymnasium. Once again, I didn't like that idea at all. In my adolescent teenage, insecure mind, I knew I would be embarrassed. What would my friends say?

How must my mother have felt? A tall, lithe, attractive woman now had to rely on a contraption with wheels to maintain some independence. Years later, as the disease progressed, we never discussed those early times. My mother never told me what it was like for her early on, when her legs refused to work as they should. Frustration, sadness, fear? How bad would it get? Did she fear she might die because of this disease that was kidnapping her basic abilities? But she made a journal entry about that pep assembly . . .

JANE—September 26, 1980: Football game Fri. Rex and I went with Ali Thurs to kickoff. I was going to take the wheelchair, Ali had a fit—said she hated it, me too

JANE—October 6, 1980: Rex took me to Pain Center at Jewish Hospital—I got a shot of novocaine and cortisone, could not even stand up tonight. The back pain was gone but . . .

JANE—October 7, 1980: felt rotten—hardly walk—pain in back not <u>so</u> bad.

JANE—October 11, 1980: I never say enough about Rex. He helps me <u>so</u> much— works so hard and never complains. He's so patient with the girls. I made an apple pie and chili for dinner.

JANE—October 15, 1980: Rex took me to the Pain Center again. I got 4 shots this time—It seemed to relieve the pain, both legs asleep.

JANE—October 20, 1980: Woke up feeling <u>great</u>. Even felt like walking around on the patio. Legs got weaker as day went on.

JANE—October 23, 1980: Sue asked me to go to lunch with her. I was scared but I need to get out and we did fine. It was great to go out, back killing me.

JANE—November 4, 1980: Election day—Reagan—

JANE—November 5, 1980: Edna took me to rehab—I am so anxious to get started in that, I will have to <u>really</u> work.

JANE—November 19, 1980: Quite a day! Rex took me to PT then to the Chase for lunch with his committee. I rested in our room at hotel—He worked that evening—MS Sports Celebrity Banquet, 810 tickets sold—Rex chaired. He did a terrific job!

The Multiple Sclerosis Sports Celebrity Banquet became an annual event that my father let Carolyn and me attend. We would arrive at the chosen hotel ballroom, donning our favorite dresses and high-heeled shoes and begin scoping for "celebrities." My father, who served on the MS Society board and chaired the event for many years, always looked so handsome in his dark suit and tie. While he shook hands with members of the St. Louis Cardinals and Blues, Carolyn and I stood wide-eyed, yearning for autographs. The dinner event included live and silent auctions to raise money for research to help end this devastating disease.

ALLISON—1980: Me and mom just had a talk. From now on I am not going to be sassy—I am going to be helpful. I love mom, dad, Diny and Carolie so much. This is going to be the best Xmas ever!

JANE—December 1980: What a wonderful Christmas we had this year. Steve & Diana came Xmas Eve—opened our gifts Xmas morning. Dad and Steve fixed Eggs Benedict for breakfast—Just a neat relaxing day. Fondue for supper—went to Franklin next day. Diana stuffed a pillow in her dress which gave them quite a shock (ha). Another fantastic Xmas there.

Every Christmas was a rerun of the one prior, though the level of fun was sometimes accelerated, if that were possible. Carolyn and I snuggled together in the same bed every Christmas Eve. This continued until we married and no longer lived at home! "Santa" would hurriedly wrap last minute gifts and carry them to the family room, where they would linger as statues until the wee hours of the morning. When we were young, Carolyn and I would wake so early that we were often sent, longfaced, back to our bedrooms for further slumber. On Christmas morning, we were not allowed to enter the family room, which held the tall pine tree covered with ornaments we had glued and glittered at Girl Scouts, until my father had inspected Santa's delivery. Once we were given the signal, we ran for our treasures. Gifts were opened one by one, so everyone could see what each package held. After a hurricane of paper and bows flooded the family room, we ate breakfast and then quickly piled into my father's Monte Carlo for the trip to Franklin, Illinois. The anticipation grew as our car veered through southern Illinois, past the soybean fields, and dried corn stalks. We were regressing into another time in history. Suddenly, the pace slowed, the tall buildings of St. Louis disappeared, and the era of simplicity came into view. We were always the last to arrive at my grandparents' home, as my aunts from Minnesota and their families traveled the week before Christmas. What a joyous reunion this was every year! My aunts each had three children, so my six cousins littered the doorway and made our arrival festive and full of excitement. Buttery sugar cookies, homemade fudge, and Grandma's caramel popcorn balls were devoured throughout the next few days, while we played Scrabble and Rook and crawled through the "haunted" basement.

1981

(My mother is forty-six and I am fourteen)

JANE—January 20, 1981: What a day this has been—Reagan inaugurated as new pres. and our 52 hostages finally free after 444 days as prisoners in Iran. I watched TV most of the day. Needed to lie around anyway, my back had been so bad. Edna took me back to therapy and pain clinic 1/19, got 3 shots—went home to bed. No pain—1/21 still no pain but I'm really taking it easy. I'm so afraid it will come back.

ALLISON—February 9, 1981: Today was Mop's [mom's nickname on occasion] birthday. C and I fixed breakfast in bed for her and dad in bed this morning. I think she had a great day. There is alot of snow, I hope we don't have school. The snow is so beautiful. I like to flirt sometimes but then I think I shouldn't. I'm confused about that.

When I was fourteen, our family began spending our spring break vacations in Sarasota, Florida. We stayed at the Harley Sandcastle, a modest hotel with only a few floors and no interior hallways. This became one of my mother's favorite destinations and mine as well. My father would reserve a room, poolside/beachfront, so we could exit our back door and instantly feel sand oozing through our toes. At nightfall, we lay in bed and listened to the surf trounce the shore. The crashing of the waves became a sing-song sleeping aid. Out front, a tiki bar with a thatched hut was positioned near the pool. As you made your way from the pool to the beach, along a concrete walkway, a snack shack sat perched in the corner. Carolyn and I used to buy foot-long hot dogs to enjoy as we lay by the pool. (Of course, as we aged, we wouldn't have been caught dead holding a foot-long hot dog while wearing a bikini). In those early years, Mom could walk out to the pool, and then with the assistance of a cane, and, eventually, the wheelchair. On occasion, my dad would wheel her out onto the beach, not an easy task in sand, if you have ever attempted it. Once I snapped a photograph of her sitting there on the beach in the wheelchair, gazing out at the gulf. She looks so angelic and peaceful, with the sun setting in shades of pink and coral in the distance.

ALLISON—July 19, 1981: I haven't written in awhile. I finished 8th grade with a smile. I made cheerleading again.

ALLISON—December 12, 1981: Well Christmas is coming up. I am really excited. I have not told you so much. 9th grade has really been great. I love it. I am popular and have a lot of friends. I fell in love for the first time in 9th grade. With Kent. Kent moved to Texas. I still love him very much but now he's going out with another girl but I think he still loves me. I loved him so much and it wasn't fake, it was real, I'm almost sure. Now I like this guy named Steve. He is super nice.

HUH!?!

1982

(My mother is forty-seven and I am fifteen)

ALLISON—April 25, 1982: I went to church with mom today, it was fun. Just me and her.

JANE—June 4, 1982: The last day of school—another milestone—I can't believe my 2 "little" girls are getting so grown up. Ali is through with Jr. High and Carolyn with elementary.

ALLISON—October 1982: Cardinals won the World Series!

In junior high and high school, I became addicted to the soap opera, *As the World Turns*. My mother had watched the daytime drama since its debut in 1956. Once the VCR was invented, Mom would record *The World* for Carolyn and me. After we arrived home from school, the three of us reviewed the excitement that had occurred during the day between doctors, nurses, evil twins, and the occasional sociopath faking paralysis. Carolyn and I added to the special effects by throwing objects at the television when our favorite couple split or an innocent pawn was arrested. Of course, we were always enjoying some kind of afterschool snack (as previously noted, these became essential at a very young age).

1983

(My mother is forty-eight and I am sixteen)

JANE—January 1983: What a weekend! A wonderful time to remember—Diana and Steve surprised us on Sunday and drove from KC to tell us we will have a grandchild in September!! I can't believe this time is near—I have looked forward to being a Grandma—I want to make and buy things now!

JANE—1983: "My memory is so bad" I keep excusing myself with this alibi but actually I think my problem is more a lack of concentration or—thinking about myself too much. So—I plan to use this book to help me remember people, thoughts, ideas etc—I really became aware that I needed to do something like this just by observing my own family. Diana by her ever thoughtfulness and concern, Rex by his constant love and patience, Allison by her eagerness to help me in every way and Carolyn by her quiet and sincere caring. Please God, help me be more <u>aware</u> of others and <u>their</u> needs.

JANE—1983: I think and wonder a lot about this—I am so lucky—I have so much—enough money, a great family—and I am happy but is it right to just enjoy life when so many people are unhappy—hungry, etc—But what can I do? Talked to Clodie [my mother's sister] about it. Must give this more thought.

JANE—1983: How much <u>can</u> I do or <u>should</u> I do to help the girls in forming individual personalities. They are what they are but some things they need to work on. Allison is so demanding and impatient. Traits I wish she could change—on the other hand she has so many good qualities—I guess she will learn to control these things. Carolyn is not too eager to help out, she finds lots of excuses but sometimes she's so willing. I think she has a sweet likeable personality at school and is well liked. Guess I want them both perfect! I must let them develop while I try to help them overcome the negative qualities. Nothing is a big problem—Allison gets pretty bossy—my main worry.

JANE—September 1983: I need to think of what I can do to help others. Some days I can't get around well at all and get so frustrated. Today I read about a boy

(18) from Parkway Central [high school] who is co-captain of the football team, nice looking—was paralyzed from waist down -skiing accident. How awful- so young and I complain. . . . Today I slept late and thought of how I love our bedroom. There was a cool breeze, birds singing. It is so airy and peaceful. Then I sat by the pool in the sun and also swam—2 hours. Beautiful, gorgeous day, 84 degrees. Roses all in bloom by the pool, pink, yellow, apricot, red and white.

JANE—September 11, 1983: Steve called at 3:30am to say they are at the hospital. Diana in labor. Diana called at 6:30. They did a cesarean at 5:30. It's a GIRL—Megan Elizabeth. Diana was shaking, I could hear it in her voice. They are so excited.

ALLISON—September 11, 1983: Diana had her baby this morning!!!! It's a girl. Yesterday Diana saw a rainbow (sign from God). This morning the phone rang at 4:00am, it was Steve. He talked like a robot. He said Diana had gone into labor and I got mom on the phone. He said they were gonna do it cicerian at 5:00. Mom told dad and I woke up Carolyn. At 6:30 they called us and told us it was a girl. Megan Elizabeth, 5:34am, 7 pounds, 13 ounces

JANE—September 16, 1983: We all drove to KC to see Megan. She is a doll and slept most of the time we were there. Spent Sunday passing Megan around.

As a teenager, I had never spent time around a baby. When I babysat for neighbors, my dependents were young children, not infants. So, my niece Megan became my first "baby" experience. Diana and Steve were living in Kansas City, roughly a four-hour drive from St. Louis. That first weekend visit we laid on my sister's bed and spent hours staring at this new arrival. We stared at her doing nothing, for days.

JANE—September 1983: Megan Elizabeth—she is such a cutie. How I wish I could have stayed there to help Diana. But what help would I be? I wish so much I was able to do that. I decided I would blow a little $$ and call Diana during the day 3 times, the first and second weeks to see how Megan is doing.

ALLISON—November 16, 1983: I've been thinking about sex a lot, I guess you can't help thinking about that—I guess I'm getting older and growing up. I'm afraid that it will happen too soon and it won't be like I expected.

1984

(My mother is forty-nine and I am seventeen)

JANE—1984: Thinking today of our planned vacation to Sarasota, it's always so much fun. The beach, seagulls, sunset, pool, can't wait. Grandma Jane and Grandpa Rex—doesn't that sound great! How can we be so lucky?

[Jane] **February 14, 1984:**
Dear Rex,
How do I love thee? Let me count the reasons why,
I can't name them all no matter how I try.
It was your good looks that first attracted me
You are still so handsome everyone will agree.
Through all these years you've provided for me
All the material needs, a home and family.
Lovely vacations that will always be
A special part of our memories.
You are very successful in your career
You give your time as a volunteer.
You help with the groceries and getting meals
Chauffeuring us no matter how you feel.
You're patient with me when I'm down and out
Your devotion to our girls leaves me no doubt.
Your thoughtfulness with the Danish you buy
You're so generous, you're quite a guy.
The years we've been together have just flown by
I'm so thankful I met you that night in July.
I'm so happy we've spent these years together
And I want to be by your side forever.
Love, Jane

ALLISON—March 3, 1984: I made a list of the boys I have kissed and dad found it—he asked what it was, I was so embarrassed!

ALLISON—March 31, 1984: Turnabout dance was awful! We got drunk afterward. Mom found out we were drunk, it was awful—she was so upset and was crying. I swore to her I would never do it again and I won't!

JANE—April 1984: We had a really great vacation in Sarasota—Us, Steve, Diana and Megan. Out to eat every night and Megan was so good til the last one. She was so tired. Had a port-a-crib for Megan, our rooms side by side. It was handy to go to the pool while she took her naps. It was a great time!

JANE—May 27, 1984: Just had a great weekend—on Friday Ali found out she made cheerleading and Carolie found out she made poms. I was so afraid one would make it and one wouldn't.

Swimming gave my mother freedom, motion, and weightlessness. Before we had our own backyard pool, in the evenings my father took my mother to the country club pool to swim laps. I have no memory of this. But my brother-in-law, who was a lifeguard at the club in those days, tells the story of how my parents would arrive around dinner time, when the pool was deserted. My father would help my mother into the water so she could have that freedom. The other lifeguards thought my mother was beautiful and that my parents appeared to be such a loving couple. The boys wondered what had "happened" to my mother. Had she been in a car accident?

In 1984 my father bought a wheelchair-assessable van, with a lift. I hated that ugly, beige van, but it gave my mother some independence. She could drive herself to the mall or the library or doctor. Mom would transfer her body from the driver's seat to the wheelchair then open the lift, which unfolded out the side of the van. The lift descended to the ground. She would wheel herself off and then use a remote control to close the lift and door. If someone parked too close to the lift side of the van, it could not be opened. This happened, despite the sign on the door warning other motorists. So, on occasion my mother would wheel herself out to the parking lot and find that some inconsiderate or unobservant soul had parked too close and she couldn't leave.

JANE—August 1984: What a great 10 days we just had. Diana and Megan came to visit. It was such fun having them here that long. Megan is starting to walk—a few steps at a time. She loves Pepper. It was fun taking her for rides in the wheelchair.

JANE—October 19, 1984: I just had to talk to someone about this—I hate to gripe to people about things that happen—I do- but know everyone would rather not hear it. So many times lately I really question my abilities as a mother. I used to think Ali and I had a perfect relationship, we talked and laughed a lot, etc. We probably have not gone anywhere in the same car 3 or 4 times since she started to drive. Today was such a pretty day. Today I was thinking how neat it would be for Ali and I to go to Crestview [Junior High School] and see Carolie's poms perform. I never mentioned it but Ali went. Why doesn't she ever ask me to go along. . . . Maybe all kids are like that and I'm too sensitive. I just don't feel a part of their lives anymore. Ali is ready for college. She is so independent and never wants to have to ask or tell where she's going. I am so thankful to have the van. I must make a new life. It has always revolved around the girls and Rex, of course. But now that I can go out I am trying to create some new interests. I like to go to the mall, Cloth World, library and now 2 weeks into Bible Study which I love so far.

In the fall of 1984, my father and I began our college "road trip." We journeyed to the University of Wisconsin in Madison; Purdue University in Lafayette, Indiana; and Indiana University in Bloomington. We toured each campus, and I instantly fell in love with IU. My forehead remained glued to the glass as we drove through the streets of the Midwestern town of Bloomington. I stared, wide-eyed at the coeds bustling to class with book bags slung over their backs. In less than one year, this would be me! I felt trapped in space between two galaxies, my childhood and my future. I wrestled with the changes occurring and feared the decisions that dangled before my eyes. Which college? Which dormitory? Which major? I felt overwhelmed but exhilarated. I longed for a fresh start, a new world! However, I didn't want that "new world" to be too far from home. IU was a mere four-hour drive, which would make occasional weekend trips home an easy task.

ALLISON—October 24, 1984: I got accepted to Indiana University!!! That's probably where I will go. I loved it when dad and I went and visited. It was so pretty.

JANE—October 29, 1984: Well, how strange life is. Only a week ago I was feeling so low, left out and not in touch with the girls—Ali has been totally different this week. She's been cheerful, happy, talkative, etc. ?? I don't know why the change but I like it. Carolie is very considerate, helpful whenever I ask her to do something and seems so much more grown up this year.

BOYS. That is why my mood changed from one minute to the next, pretty much until I turned forty. I liked boys from a very young age, and the desire to have them like me directed my life's course for many years. My journals are saturated with my thoughts on boys and men: who l liked and didn't like, who I kissed, who I couldn't live without, and who I no longer wanted to live with. My relationships with men plagued my journal writing. When a relationship was failing, or had failed, that is when my soul searching sprang into action. Often, when I was alone and had time to marinate on other subjects is when my best writing occurred. Since this book is a tribute to my mother, I won't dwell on the numerous journal entries I made with my concerns on "whether he would call or not." I can't imagine dating in the era of texting, Twitter and Facebook!

*ALLISON—January 9, **1976**: I went to school. Mark seemed like he liked me. Mark liked me in gym and lots of other places in school. When I got home I had two Ding Dongs and hot chocolate and watched a good movie on tv. Carolyn only got 1 Ding Dong. [I am nine years old!]*

*ALLISON—January 20, **1976**: Mom woke me up and I said I was having a good dream but I didn't tell her that it was about Mark. I love Mark. [still nine years old]*

*ALLISON—February 16, **1976**: We did not have school and I kissed a boy named Jerry. I kissed Jerry because he tackled me and I said if he didn't get off me, I was going to kiss him so I did. Jerry is in the forth grade right now.*

So, that is where it all began I suppose. BOYS.

1984 masqueraded as my "last" Christmas at home, as I would be going off to college in 1985. Though I continued to spend many more years at home with my parents, I believe my mother viewed this year as a turning point and presented me with this poem:

[Jane] **December 1984**
Merry Christmas, my dear sweet Ali.
This is a very special one.
There'll be some changes before Christmas comes again,
Most I hope will be fun.

Because this is such a special time,
I want to use this little rhyme,
To tell you how you play such a big part,
In bringing Christmas so close to my heart.
I think of other years gone by,
I feel some sadness I can't deny,
Bear with me a moment while I pause,
To remember the days you believed in Santa Clause.
You got so excited and so did we,
But that hasn't changed a bit you see,
Your enthusiasm made it so special then,
It makes it the same as it's always been.
You have a beautiful gift deep down inside,
Being a child at heart is something you shouldn't hide.
Our world is so troubled and the future may look unclear,
But you have what it takes to succeed, my dear.
Don't forget with your determination and drive,
Always keep that child-like spirit alive
Always keep cool and calm,
And remember I love you,
Mom

1985

(My mother is fifty and I am eighteen)

JANE—February 1985: I should be sure to write this in here—Rex and the girls gave me a surprise luncheon at the club for my 50th! It was so neat.

ALLISON—March 15, 1985: Today I went to make up a psychology test and for some reason my teacher started talking to me. I kinda started crying—it was bad. I don't know why. I told him how I was so afraid of dying, but I didn't know why.

Thoughts of death and dying tormented me throughout my adolescence. And though I refused to believe my mother would die from multiple sclerosis, I suppose, deep down, I knew it was possible. My fears however, seemed to focus on my own demise. I had been raised under the umbrella of faith in God and everlasting life, but often I could not grasp the concept. Where will I be? Will I know others? Will I realize I have died? When these demons entered my mind, I had to feverishly work to reroute my visions, mind my faith, and just pray.

ALLISON—April 6, 1985: We are in St. Thomas! It's GREAT! It is so beautiful, but I keep thinking about 2 guys [at school]. Carolyn and I haven't really met any cute guys—there are mostly ugly older ones.

JANE—April 27, 1985: So long since I have written—this spring we had such a great vacation to St. Thomas. So much of it was great fun and great to be with Ali and Carolie. But we had several days when it seemed like all we did was argue— Ali could get in the worst moods for some reason? So many times I feel she doesn't appreciate what all she has or gets to do? I get so upset if I think of my condition— very much. I know it's worse. I went to Cloth World yesterday—didn't feel good, took me 2 hours to get in and back in the wheelchair. I just don't know what to do. I keep thinking I need exercise but so often I don't feel like doing any. Carolie had her first date last night— 9th grade dance—I hope so much that next year she will want to talk to me, etc. She and Ali are so close now and I'm glad. Just hope they aren't lonely next year.

JANE—April 1985: I want to write down these feelings I have right now—I may forget them and someday maybe it will help someone—I know a lot of my feelings are caused by Ali & C ages. They are growing up and wanting to be independent. Still I can't help it—I used to feel angry that I couldn't do more <u>physically</u> for all of the family but at least I felt they needed me—as a mother— to talk to and help them make decisions, etc. Now, I feel rather useless—and many times—lonely. Diana understands because she <u>is</u> a mother. I don't mean to feel sorry for myself (this—Ali hates) and I <u>am</u> so lucky in many ways. It's difficult to put into words. Part of my problem is I'm lucky to have one day a week when I feel <u>really good.</u> God! I wish I could get better. It's hard to explain how I feel— guess I really don't know.

JANE—May 7, 1985: Just a few days since last entry and things seem different— We 4 spent Sunday afternoon by the pool—great day, Rex got KF Chicken, just enjoyed being together.

JANE—June 11, 1985: Ali's graduation—lovely evening—held on the Lafayette ball field. Can't believe time has passed so quickly.

JANE—June 1985: Rex took me to see Dr. Trotter—hadn't been for 2 years. Just thought he might have some idea for new medication, etc. He says I must start exercising or I will lose the use of my legs. I <u>have</u> to get busy on that. Ali took me to a movie today, "Fletch"—I really enjoyed going with her.

JANE—July 3, 1985: Diana, Steve, Megan came late—Megan was cute—she climbed right on my lap for a ride. We had such a good visit. Fun on the 4th, swam, barbecued ribs, made ice cream, watched fireworks. Megan loved the fireworks. We all went to the zoo Saturday. That was really fun—Megan loved the monkeys. She is beginning to put 2 or 3 words together.

One of my favorite memories is the process by which my mother awakened us each 4th of July. Our bedrooms were just off the hallway that led from the family room. The stereo system was perched in the family room, and my mother would insert a cassette tape of Lee Greenwood's song, "God Bless the USA." She would crank the volume to capacity so Carolyn and I would be called out of our slumber to "I'm proud to be an American because at least I know I'm free!" Once the Greenwood song ended, tunes of marching bands commenced, and this continued most of the morning. My mother loved musicals, and so very often, the tunes from *Cats, Miss Saigon* or *Showboat* would blast through our home as well.

ALLISON—July 23, 1985: God I have to write how I feel. I was looking for a ticket mom had lost and I ran across her journal. She had read parts to me before so I didn't really think it was real private. There was a lot about me and Car and how I sometimes got in bad moods, etc. But there was a part on how mom and me didn't really have a good relationship anymore—she said it was because Carolie and I were so close and I didn't really share much with mom. But I love her so so so much and dad too, I don't know why I don't appreciate them more. I wish mom and I got along better or like we used to. I want her to be my friend again. I am really trying to be a better kinder person. I hope mom won't get mad if she finds out I read her diary—it wasn't my place but I might not have realized how badly I've been acting if I hadn't read it.

JANE—August 1985: Diana, Steve, Megan came on Wednesday night and stayed til Sunday. Friday evening A, C and D went to a movie and Dad, Steve and I had Megan—she kept wanting "Mama." We all took her for a walk, her on my lap in the wheelchair and of course, "Pep" had to be with us.

ALLISON—August 17, 1985: One week from tomorrow! I go to school!! I am so nervous and I'm really worried about getting homesick, I know I will. Diana and Megan come tomorrow Diana is pregnant again!!!!!

JANE—August 26, 1985: Here we are (Rex, Ali and I) in Bloomington to "deliver" Ali to college. What a terrific summer we have had, but it went too fast. A, C and I had lots of days by the pool together—I loved the times together. Was so sad to see Ali and Carolie leave each other. Carolie will be so lonesome and Ali is so nervous.

ALLISON—August 27, 1985: I'm at college—I'm so so homesick. I miss mom, dad, Carolyn, Diana, Megan and Steve so much. And mom and dad only left this afternoon. I hope it gets easier. I had a long talk with Diana about everything. It was good to talk to her. I hope I don't always feel this homesick.

JANE—August, 1985: came back Tuesday, so hard to leave her—I will miss her so. She called at 9:30 crying cause she was lonesome. When we got home we discovered Carolyn had a party here!! Beer and soda all gone. Can't believe C would do that! We grounded her—2 weeks???

JANE—Labor day weekend 1985: We are letting C redecorate her room—she painted it—Rex wallpapered, got new carpet and waterbed. Good way to punish someone??

Though I struggled my freshman year of college . . . a new town, a new state, a new world, the one feeling I distinctly remember is the independence I had been granted. I recall it as though it were delivered to me on a silver platter. The first week I walked from my dormitory, a tall building at the edge of campus, past the School of Business and the unusually shaped Art Museum to the IU Student Union to purchase books and supplies. The IU campus is beautiful, and the September breezes blew in the excitement of a new school year. I was on my own. I didn't know a soul in this small Indiana city and I didn't have to report to anyone. My parents were miles away. I could linger in the bookstore, stop for a chocolate frozen yogurt, or simply watch lovers picnicking in the adjacent fields. I was free to do as I pleased. I wasn't required to inform anyone when I would be home or where I was going. This was not something I had ever experienced, and the feeling was amazing. To this day, I can almost taste that independence, like it's a ripe, luscious peach.

ALLISON—September 17, 1985: I'm really confused about something. What I'm doing at I.U. I really feel lost in this huge crowd of people. It's so different from high school. It seems all the things I prided myself on: dancing, cheerleading, all my friends, boyfriends—are nothing here. So many better dancers, so many better people. I hate being a freshman, the youngest. It seems like I've lost all sight of my future. I know it sounds serious, but it is. I can't imagine living here for 4 years. It just seems like I'm on a long trip, soon to go home and go back to LHS with all my friends and family. Things were so easy then, I love school now, but it's not my normal life. Today in Theatre [class] we had to remember details about the day of our graduation—I almost cried, I know I had tears in my eyes. That was a great day, being with all my friends, making that big transition in my life. College seemed so far away then—but now I'm living all that excitement and nervousness, it's all here.

JANE—October 24, 1985: Rex took the day off after 3 nights of World Series. Beautiful day—We drove to Washington MO for lunch, then to winery, farm for cider, gourds and corn, bakery for bread and cookies. It was a nice day.

JANE—Thanksgiving 1985: We all went to KC Thursday, Diana fixed a great meal. Their house is fixed so cute. Megan was so fun. Took her to see Santa Friday.

She was on my lap when he came into the mall area. He came over and talked to us and she talked so much like "I leave you cookies and hot chocolate"—but she didn't want to sit on his lap.

ALLISON—November 30, 1985: Well tomorrow I go back to school, then 2 & ½ weeks and I'm home again for Christmas! I really had a great time this week being with mom, dad and Carolyn. On Thanksgiving we went to Diana and Steve's. Megan is adorable. We had so much fun playing with her. She can say so much! She talks so good. Carolyn and I taught her to say, "I'm sure." [spoken with a 'Valley Girl' intonation]

JANE—December 8, 1985: Rex gave Carolyn red roses [her sixteenth birthday] he cooked steak and bought a cake for her. He had to leave at 5 to go to Portland, Oregon. Don't know how I could live without him.

And this is the last journal entry I have from my mother.

1986

(My mother is fifty-one and I am nineteen)

ALLISON—April 14, 1986: Diana had a baby 4/9/86, a girl; Emily Jane. I can't wait to see her!!

Mom loved that Emily was named in her honor and always jokingly placed the emphasis on Emily's middle name when speaking about her . . . Emily JANE.

Megan and Emily blossomed into my miniature models, dolls, and dance students. I loved dressing them in outrageous outfits; styling their hair with crimping irons, braids, and bows; and painting their young faces with ruby-red lip gloss and glistening blue eye shadow. They were avid pupils, watching my every move as I choreographed dance routines for them to perform at our family "recitals." One of our first performances was a jazzy number to "Straight Up," sung by Paula Abdul. Megan was around age five and Emily three. After a few hours of my stellar instruction, they executed the moves with precision (well, sort of) in a "living room show" for their parents and grandparents. An interesting anecdote, in 2010 (twenty-one years after their debut), the three of us performed our "Straight Up" dance at Megan's wedding reception. Not a move forgotten.

[Jane] June 3, 1986: <u>Happy Anniversary</u>
Thanks for sharing 30 years of your life
I'm so happy and proud to be your wife.
I always knew you would give me the moon
If ever I asked you to
I hope you know I feel the same
There's nothing I wouldn't do.
What gift could I give you
To express how I feel
Something lasting and personal
Sentimental, yet real.
Still I know you are quite a practical guy

So I thought real estate might be a good buy.
You're now the owner of a small moon site
Just get out your telescope and view it at night.
If you come to the point when you've had it
And no peaceful place can you find
Just take me along and we'll fly to the moon
And leave all our cares behind.
Love, Jane

ALLISON—October 22, 1986: Mom was in the hospital last week for a "tune-up" (as her doctor says) they drugged her and put her on all this medicine and now she's worse than when she went in. She's out of the hospital but she just has to lay in bed and can't really do anything. I miss her so much—I'm so scared. It makes me feel so bad that I can't be with her. Things aren't too great in my life right now— except I love my friends here [college].

Most of the nurses were compassionate caretakers who worked to make my mother comfortable. But, as expected, there were always those who displayed such negative attitudes that we wondered why they had chosen health care as a career. My mother was a magnificent eye-roller. A word needn't be uttered and we could capture her thoughts on a person. There were several nurses who would enter mom's room and speak to her as though she were deaf or had the intelligence of a third grader. Eye rolling . . . making us all laugh upon the nurse's exit. Mom's neurologist, though a topnotch specialist, was an odd duck with a strange way about him. He received more eye rolling than most, as he left her bedside, with his quirky smile and awkward personality. Who wants their neurologist to be charming and good-looking anyway? I've always felt, the less attractive and weirder, the more time that person spent studying in medical school.

1987

(My mother is fifty-two and I am twenty)

ALLISON—January 7, 1987: Well it's the new year—1987. A lot has happened. Mom went into the hospital last Friday. Saturday was really bad; she couldn't talk or move, it seemed like she didn't even know who we were. It was the scariest thing ever. We weren't sure if she was going to make it. She's better now, but still in the hospital. Thank God, it was all the praying that kept her with us— I know it!

ALLISON—January 26, 1987: Mom is doing a lot better than when she was in the hospital but I think dad is going to hire a nurse for her, for while Carolyn is at school. I guess she can't really be alone for awhile. I just want to be strong, confident and happy with myself and my life. I have so much, but I just don't know what to do with it. I mean I feel so lucky with what I've been given, I think I'm pretty selfish sometimes.

It was during this semester of college when I wandered into a large auditorium to attend my first criminology course, an "elective" I had chosen. Up to this point, I was majoring in ballet, a course of study I suspected, disappointed my father. I feared that he believed he was paying a hefty tuition toward a degree that would take me nowhere in life. I had danced my way through adolescence and loved every minute of it, but this was different. Realistically, what would I do with a college degree in ballet? I enjoyed dance, but as the other ballerinas twirled around me, I knew I did not have the talent to succeed in the dancing world, New York or Los Angeles. The criminology "elective" altered my life's path. I was intrigued and captivated from the first hour of class and quickly registered for more . . . crime, psychology, forensics. I wanted to learn all I could about the criminal mind and the "why" of it all.

ALLISON—February 10, 1987: I went home this past weekend for mom's birthday. It was fun but really short. Mom didn't feel real great and she was afraid she might have to go in the hospital. I don't think that will happen. But it's really scary. Mom said she was afraid of dying lately—I felt so bad because I really didn't get to talk to her.

ALLISON—March 21, 1987: Mom is doing better since Christmas. She has her bad days but she's a lot better since then. I wonder if she gets scared sometimes, about being sick. I don't know.

ALLISON—April 3, 1987: I just had my 20th birthday. A little more than a ¼ of my life is gone. It's strange. I feel like I haven't really done anything spectacular or important with my life.

ALLISON—April 17, 1987: Today is Good Friday. I'm at home because Easter is this Sunday. Mom wasn't very good at all when I got home today. She hasn't slept I guess. She was crying and I felt bad. I don't know what to do for her. I wish someday she would just wake up and she'd be better. Everything would be good, it would be like a miracle. I know God can perform miracles, but I also know he has his reasons not to, but what is the reason? How can there be a logical one in mom's case?

ALLISON—May 18, 1987: Mom and I have been talking a lot. I'm so glad. I love talking with her—I feel closer to her.

ALLISON—June 19, 1987: Something new has happened. I think God talked to mom. These past two weeks she's had so much spirit. She wants to go on vacation, her and dad are redecorating the family room and she's not afraid of anything. Sometimes I have no patience or I don't listen. At first when mom told me about this [fearlessness] I was scared. But now I guess I see that it's great. But in a way it scares me because I don't want this to be God's way of preparing mom for death. I guess the best thing is to be sure I do all that I can for mom and then I'll be at peace with whatever happens. Of course, no matter what happens I'll always want more time with mom. But, I'm still being optimistic—I'm praying that mom will start feeling better soon.

ALLISON—July 4, 1987: Mom is feeling better—she looks better and she really acts better. She went to a hypnotist to help her sleep; it sounded really neat. But today dad went into emergency surgery. His appendix burst. Carolyn and I took him over. I'm scared. I think he's going to be ok—it was so sad leaving him there alone at the hospital. He looked so lonely. And on the 4th! It rained anyway tho, but still, I wish he could have seen some fireworks. God please help dad get better . . . soon. He has to be there for a week–10 days.

And that is when the panic attacks surfaced. One of my greatest fears hovered on the horizon. What if something happened to my father? How would we cope, how would we take care of mom? After my father was hospitalized for his appendectomy, this thought began to haunt me. Perhaps he wasn't invincible.

ALLISON—July 12, 1987: Dad came home today! Yay!! He has to miss 2 weeks of work. He's still worn out and kind of run down, but at least he's home. Thursday night at about 3am I was taken to the hospital in an ambulance. I could hardly breathe and I was shaking—actually I was hyperventilating but they had to take blood and x-rays and they had to do an EKG, this heart rate thing. But I'm ok and I came back home after an hour and a half. It was scary, I'd never been in an ambulance before. I guess it was all from stress and fatigue.

ALLISON—July 13, 1987: I went to a movie with Lori tonight, but I kept thinking I was going to hyperventilate again. I was nervous the whole time. I still need to do something about my fear. It really bothers me. I know I need to have more faith.

ALLISON—August 14, 1987: Mom was really depressed today. Carolyn and I talked to her for a couple hours by the pool. She was saying some <u>really</u> negative things. I think she feels better now. I hope so. She's been doing so good lately.

ALLISON—September 9, 1987: I'm going home this weekend for Diana and Megan's birthdays (29 and 4). I'm excited but Diana said mom isn't doing very good—or that she hasn't been doing too great lately.

As I mentioned, though I selfishly disliked my mother's wheelchair, Megan and Emily loved it. My mother would sit in her chair, with both granddaughters positioned in her lap. She wheeled them throughout the house, so they could inspect her treasures. Their favorite stop was my mother's tall cherry wood and glass cabinet, which cradled her angel and music box collections. Once they arrived at this destination, they would carefully wind up all of the music boxes. The melodies then played through our home, each finishing their delicate tune at a different moment in time. For these two young girls, the wheelchair brought excitement and a journey into a magical world where their feet didn't touch the ground. If only I could have peered through the Looking Glass and viewed it that way. . .

ALLISON—October 10, 1987: Like I said, I'm at home, I love coming home but there's something about being here that makes me feel depressed or kind of sad or something, maybe scared is the word. This morning something weird happened. Mom was leaning over and she like passed out or kind of fainted or something. Dad got her into bed and she slept 2 hours. She seems better now, but that's so strange. I always seem to think about dying when I come home. I love my family, but it makes me afraid to come home, which sounds stupid. But I guess I'm afraid I'll be afraid.

ALLISON—October 11, 1987: Dad and Diana took mom to the hospital tonight, she's had 2 seizures, they're like she almost passes out. She has to stay there awhile, well for a couple of days. I'm kind of scared. I feel like this MS is making mom different. I don't understand any of it. I thought mom would be physically handicapped, but now it seems like it's her mind too, she can't remember things. We went to brunch this morning and after that seizure mom didn't even remember we went to brunch. That's so scary.

As MS heightened its assault, the porcelain angel's significance grew. Though this white, delicate beauty initially sat frozen in the sterile glass cabinet, she was now transformed into my mother's heavenly guardian. Each hospital stay beckoned her to my mother's bedside, keeping watch when we could not.

ALLISON—October 16, 1987: Wednesday the Cardinals won the National League pennant and they'll play Minnesota in the World Series. YAY!!!

ALLISON—October 27, 1987: Dad came this weekend for homecoming—we had the best time. And IU won the game!! Now we're 1st in the Big Ten!!! Cards lost the Series. I was so sad when dad left.

ALLISON—November 2, 1987: Carolyn called tonight—we talked for an hour and a half. God I miss her! I feel so sorry for her tho. From what Carolyn said, things with mom are getting worse. Mom can't get up or down by herself at all. God please be with her and dad and Carolyn and Diana too. They're all right there and I know how that must feel. Who does dad talk to? How is he doing it? And mom too. Just to lay there all day and all night. What kind of a life is that God? I don't understand????

ALLISON—November 8, 1987: Night time. I talked to mom and dad tonight, mom could hardly talk. I cried for about an hour and half afterwards. It makes me very sad. I want to be able to remember when mom was ok. I miss her.

ALLISON—November 21, 1987: I got home tonight. I have a week off for Thanksgiving. Mom is worse than I expected. Dad said she has been this way for about 2 weeks. It's like she doesn't know what's going on. She asks some questions, but when I say things to her I feel like she doesn't comprehend it.

ALLISON—November 30, 1987: Mom was better by the time I left but I don't know how it will be at Christmas.

ALLISON—December 17, 1987: Mom is in intensive care—I can't get a hold of anyone and no one has called me so I don't know all the details. I called Diana and her neighbor was there and told me what happened. I guess mom had those seizures again.

ALLISON—December 19, 1987: I'm home now. I've seen mom 3 times. She's still in intensive care. She has this respirator tube in her mouth, a tube in her nose, an IV to feed her and these heart rate suction things on her—it is so unfair. She can't talk to us and we're not sure if she can understand us. Her doctor said she can't really understand language, I don't know if she knows who we are. Last night she would smile and make some facial expressions, and she'd squeeze dad's hand when he told her to, but this morning she wasn't respondent at all. She wouldn't even really look at us. She just stared—then tonight she would smile and imitate us nodding our heads but she didn't understand when we told her to squeeze dad's hand. Dr. Trotter said he's optimistic and he wouldn't lie about the situation. Thursday morning mom had 10 seizures, dad told me that when she started having them he thought she was gonna die. My father is the strongest person in this world. There is no reason whatsoever that my parents should have to go through this. I feel so sorry for mom, I keep picturing her in that hospital bed staring at me. She's always been there for me and I just wish that I had been more patient with her; like at Thanksgiving—I wish I had talked to her more and been with her more. Please let her be ok. Poor dad, he must be so scared. I feel so sorry for him. I'm sure it never leaves his mind, it's always there. Mom isn't going to be home for Christmas. Though I don't think she knows it's Christmastime. This whole thing has sure made me realize the real meaning of Christmas, it's not presents or shopping—those things seem so trivial. I get angry with God sometimes. How can he let this happen to someone like mom. I wish I understood.

The porcelain angel by her side.

ALLISON—Christmas 1987, night time: MOM IS SO MUCH BETTER! I'M SO ENCOURAGED! This is a great Christmas gift. We went to see mom this evening. She was laughing, she knew who we were and talked to us—she's still very confused. She didn't want us to leave. She's still in ICU. I felt so bad for dad last night; just imagine his 1st Christmas Eve without mom in over 30 years. He told me he was sad. Mom knows it's Christmas but it doesn't seem to bother her too much.

1988

(My mother is fifty-three and I am twenty-one)

ALLISON—January 1, 1988: Happy New Year! Dad was being kind of sentimental last night. I guess just because he couldn't be with mom. I felt sorry for him but mom is doing so much better, even better than before she went into the hospital. I'm so thankful.

ALLISON—January 4, 1988: Hopefully, mom will be able to come home tomorrow! I hope so.

ALLISON—February 7, 1988: Mom went into the hospital again yesterday. Now she's gonna be there for her birthday. When is it gonna stop? It made me really upset today. I went for a drive, it made me feel better. I just drove out in the country and listened to Amy Grant music.

ALLISON—February 21, 1988: Last night I hyperventilated again—I was so scared. I just breathed in a bag and I was ok. I don't understand why it happens to me?? I really miss my family.

ALLISON—March 19, 1988: Mom is in the hospital again. I guess she was just weak from the MS but they're doing some tests. I talked to her yesterday and she started to cry. I feel so sorry for her and for dad. I'm gonna go home next weekend.

ALLISON—March 26, 1988: I forgot to write about my friend Roger. The week before spring break I saw him at the library. That night Kay [my college friend] called me to tell me that Roger's mom killed herself. I couldn't get it out of my mind. It made me cry. What could have been so bad? She'll never see what he does with his life or how he grows up, what he'll do. Roger must feel like he's failed as a son. What is he gonna do? This will affect him for the rest of his life. He must have so many questions, they'll never be answered—he must be so angry. Suicide is so unfair to those left behind. I think it's a cop out. Didn't she know that God won't give us anything that we can't handle. Futures can fall down so easily. This really affected me—I'm losing my mother and Roger's mother took herself away from him. How he must feel. . . . I'm at home, I'm at the hospital though. Mom is still here, but she seems pretty good.

ALLISON—March 27, 1988: Only an hour and half til I'm 21!! Mom was pretty good physically this weekend but not mentally. They've been giving her some drugs that make her hallucinate.

The older I got, the more aggressively MS attacked my mother. I couldn't say exactly when she stopped walking. For a while, she had a cart with wheels that she could place things on and then push through the house. She tired easily and, yes, there were falls. Times when she had attempted to accomplish too much, lost her balance or strength, and crumbled to the floor. The worst was when this occurred and no one was home. My sister or I would arrive home from school and find Mom, helpless on the floor. So eventually, she used the wheelchair more and more and then she could no longer walk. Luckily, our home was a ranch style so she didn't have to conquer stairs. My dad had a small ramp installed outside their bedroom door so she could wheel herself out to our pool.

ALLISON—October 27, 1988: Mom and dad are so great. Mom is doing really good but I feel like I disappoint dad because I spend so much $. I'm trying to cut down.

ALLISON—November 9, 1988: When I was home last weekend mom and I talked on Sunday. She was telling me how she wants to walk someday. She said that she wants to be able to walk when Carolyn and I get married. She said she wants to walk with our babies and hold them not sit in the wheelchair and hold them. I felt sorry for her because she seemed sad and it makes me sad. I wish God would give her the chance to walk again.

As the years slid by, Mom could no longer transfer herself into the wheelchair. My sisters, my father or I would lift her under the arms and transfer her body to the wheelchair. On occasion, she had some strength and could partially assist, but sometimes she was almost lifeless, like a noodle. Other times, during a transfer, something funny would strike us and we would both be laughing so hard, she would almost end up on the floor. My mother had a great sense of humor.

Once my mother could no longer move herself out of bed, most of her independence was lost. There was no Internet, nor cellular telephones, so she had no real access to the outside world. During the harsh, cold of winter, when temperatures were frigid and ice blanketed the streets, my mother often did not leave the house for a month or more. She watched television and movies and loved to plan things while lying in bed. She decorated the house with visions in her head and by pouring over catalogs. She made lists and wrote poems, often by memory when she couldn't sleep. She rented video tapes so she could learn about the wonders of other countries and study the U.S. presidents. She memorized Bible verses and organized weekly Bible study at our church. Initially, in 1984, she attended the study but eventually she could no longer drive to church. It was then that the five women from the Bible study began coming to our home every Thursday. This continued for almost fifteen years. Those five women, Martha, June, Donna, Edna, and Tina became another avenue for my mother to access the world beyond our front door, other than my father and sisters and me. They shared her triumphs and struggles. They could not predict from one week to the next how my mother's health would be. Some days they would arrive to find the vibrant, cheerful woman my mother was and other days, they would find her struggling, in pain, and less determined.

1989

(My mother is fifty-four and I am twenty-two)

ALLISON—January 14, 1989: Mom was in the hospital this past week. She got out today, I talked to her and she sounded <u>so good.</u> I'm so encouraged. Her voice was really strong and she didn't seem confused or anything. We are all going to Sarasota in March! I <u>cannot</u> wait! Mom, dad, Carolyn and I are going then Diana, Steve, Megan and Emily are meeting us there! It will be so great! Please God help mom be strong for our trip! I'm so nervous about law school. I've sent all my applications now I guess I just sit back and wait. It drives me crazy so I try not to think about it. I just want one of the ones I really like to accept me. What will I do if I don't get in anywhere? I know that is being really negative, but I'm scared!!

ALLISON—January 23, 1989: I talked to mom tonight. She sounded great! Even her memory seems better. I <u>cannot wait</u> til Florida!!!!

ALLISON—February 12, 1989: I had a great weekend at home!! Thursday night for mom's birthday, we (mom, dad and I) went to dinner. It was <u>so good.</u> And we got to really talk and laugh. It was so wonderful being with them. Mom is doing <u>so good</u>—It's a miracle! It really is because she's on no new medicine, she's just doing better. She wants to walk so badly. She's like her old self again, like I always remember her . . . I've been denied by 2 law schools and that makes me upset, but I know God has something in mind for me—something good. Maybe it's not law school. I know there are lots of other things I can do. . . . I'm not going to let it get me down.

ALLISON—March 8, 1989: Another denial today—that's five. But I got a letter from Pepperdine that said my application was on hold—for further review. Kind of promising . . . . Mom had a seizure last night. I think dad was really nervous. I guess she's pretty good now, I was scared too. It's so strange that she has been doing so good and then that would happen all of a sudden.

ALLISON—March 16, 1989: We're in Sarasota now and having a great time! The weather is great!

Though my parents traveled when they were young and took us girls on wonderful family vacations, I'm quite sure they did not get to explore as much of the world as they would have liked. But even after my mother's disease had progressed, they were able to travel and on one occasion went to California. Upon their return, my mother described this scene to me. . . . They are at an upscale restaurant in Los Angeles, quaint, but upscale. White tablecloths, superb food, impressive wine list, knowledgeable wait staff. . . . My mother has no strength in her hands, as was often the case in the later years, so my father has to feed her. This never seemed to phase my father. Though my mother often said it bothered her as she wanted to care for him. Other patrons could see my mother was disabled as she sat in her wheelchair with her hands clumsily laid in her lap. So dad takes a few bites, then lifts mom's fork and feeds her, raises the wine glass to her lips, and lets her slowly sip. Near the end of their meal, a woman, a stranger, approaches their table and says, "I have been watching the two of you and this is the greatest expression of love I have ever witnessed." I wonder who that woman was? Does she still think of my parents when she thinks of love? I hope so. If I mentioned this scene to my father, he would probably deny it or laugh. He would never take credit for being so genuine. For him, that is just what a loving husband does. So, needless to say, my sisters and I grew up with a keen sense of how a decent man should behave, react, love, and stand by.

ALLISON—April 1, 1989: I can't believe I graduate in a month. High school graduation seems like yesterday. 4 years here. . . . I never thought I'd make it thru my freshman year!! That was so terrible, I sure have grown a lot since then. And since high school . . . it's amazing how different I am and how I haven't changed. It seems weird but I think I was outgoing and independent in high school, then introverted and dependent as a freshman and sophomore, now I'm "me" again! . . . I hope I'm gonna get married someday. I want to have a prince charming. I guess I want a fairytale life. Who doesn't? I'm really scared about law school, my future. I'm going to talk to my advisor on Monday, I guess I'll see what she has to say. I need to have something to hope for when I graduate.

ALLISON—April 10, 1989: I was walking through campus today thinking about . . . life. I remember those months before high school graduation, and now, 4 years later, 1989—I'm in the same situation, 3 weeks short of graduation. I can't believe it has been 4 years. It has really flown by. The difference at this graduation is that, then, I knew where I was going. I had something to look ahead to—college.

And now college is over. I wish I knew where I was going, it would make graduation even more than it will be. Lately I've been thinking about attending graduate school, maybe because I want to stay in the college atmosphere. I guess I'm not ready to leave yet. I haven't had enough of college life. Perhaps everyone feels that way when they prepare to graduate? I'm really frustrated.

ALLISON—April 26, 1989: I want so badly to be on my own, to pay my own expenses and everything. I'm not being ungrateful for the things my parents do for me, I just want to be on my own. I wish I knew where to go. This feeling is so strong inside me, it's amazing. I'm dreading the summer. I don't like worrying about my future. I know the future should be your friend, I just haven't been able to come to terms with that.

ALLISON—May 4, 1989: In a half hour I will take my last final exam of my college career! Yippee! Carolyn, Diana, mom and dad are coming tomorrow. Two days til graduation. I can't believe it. I have such mixed feelings about graduation. I wish I could be more excited about it. I wish I had some idea what the future holds for me. This has definitely been my best school year. It is so hard to accept change; knowing things will never again be as they are now. No matter how hard you try, you can't make things stay the same. It is a scary feeling, having no control. Sometimes I feel like I'm dying inside, like I'm losing my spirit.

ALLISON—May 8, 1989: Well, I'm home now. I have strep throat. It kind of ruined my graduation. Saturday, May 6, it snowed!! So, my graduation was inside.

ALLISON—June 19, 1989: "Carpe Diem—Seize the Day, Make your life extraordinary." The play goes on and on, so that you may contribute a verse, what will your verse be?

I had just seen the movie, *Dead Poets Society* and was struck by these words. My mother and I both struggled with how we would make an impact on the lives of those around us, or the world as a whole. How could we be used for the greater good? This plagued her often, being homebound and disabled, I know she feared she was not contributing her verse. How mistaken she was.

ALLISON—June 22, 1989: Mom has been pretty down since she got back from Minnesota. Dad is in London so I'm sure that has something to do with it. I talk to her and try to inspire her but it doesn't seem to help lately. I know she *wishes she could do more and just be farther along with improvements. She wants to walk <u>so badly.</u>*

ALLISON—June 28, 1989: What to do with my life? The biggest question right now. Presently I have no real purpose to my life. I need to have a job or something. I feel so lost. . . . I'm so frustrated. But I'm trying to be happy, not worry. I really need to do something worthwhile before I go crazy! I should just stop whining about everything and <u>do</u> something about it.

ALLISON—July 6, 1989: I'm on a train to Chicago. Natalie [my college roommate] is picking me up. This train ride is pretty neat, I can't remember the last time I was on a train. Sometimes, like right now, today, on this train, I <u>love</u> being by myself. I'm <u>rarely</u> lonely when I'm alone. It is so strange to watch all these tiny towns sail by, to see people in them and wonder about the lives they lead—so different from mine, in so many ways. It is frightening to think of all the things I'll never experience in my life—but I'm <u>so lucky,</u> I'll experience a lot more than some (and I have). I <u>never</u> want my life to be dull, that may be one of my worst fears! . . . I can see Chicago! The Sears tower! Wow!

ALLISON—July 26, 1989: I called the FBI today. They are going to send me an application. I need to find a job, but I really want something in my field. This is ridiculous, I get out of college and I can't even find a job!

ALLISON—August 14, 1989: Today I went to the DEA [Drug Enforcement Administration] and got an application. I would <u>love</u> to do that. If I was able to get that job I would have to go to Virginia for a 14 week training period.

ALLISON—August 30, 1989: I feel like I'm waiting for something exciting to happen in my life. I know I've got to <u>make</u> things happen. But how?! I don't want to let a minute go by—I want to use my time and make my days have worth.

ALLISON—September 14, 1989: Diana and Steve are moving to Tulsa, Oklahoma in November. They're going there September 28 to look for a house and I'm going with them. I'll watch the girls during the day while they look. I can't wait! Megan started kindergarten this year. Mom hasn't been doing very good lately. Sometimes when I look at her and how weak she is I wonder if she's going to make it to Christmas. I know that is an awful thing to say—I don't understand how she can be so bad. And her memory is terrible. I find myself hardly ever talking to her because I know she won't remember what I said.

ALLISON—September 28, 1989: I'm in the airport waiting for my flight to Tulsa. I have about 45 minutes. I'm excited for this trip. I like going to the airport—every walk of life is represented here. I can't believe I didn't write this! I got a letter from the DEA and I got accepted for an interview!

ALLISON—November 12, 1989: Mom is in the hospital. She went in Wednesday. She has just been so weak. I hope she gets out soon—I hate to think of her in there at night and alone. I had my interview with the DEA and I got the job! More on that later . . .

ALLISON—November 13, 1989: My interview with the DEA went well and I basically got the job. Yes! I was a nervous wreck! But I guess I did ok. Now they have to do a background search on me, it may take 6 months so I'm gonna go ahead and go back to school and start towards my Masters Degree.

ALLISON—November 14, 1989: I'm so nervous about this DEA job. If I take it, I feel like I will be watching my back for the rest of my life. Maybe not but it is a very dangerous job. Life decisions! Yuk!

ALLISON—November 19, 1989: It is the Sunday before Thanksgiving and mom is in intensive care. I was just in there to see her. I feel sick to my stomach. She mumbles and yells but isn't really making any sense. I can hardly stand to be in there and see her like that. Dr. Trotter said he's pretty sure she'll pull through and be fine. I'm scared.

Barnes Hospital had become almost a second home for my parents. For me, driving there brought anxiety. I never knew how she would be. I would maneuver my car down highway 40, to the city of St. Louis, pull into the underground garage, and search for a spot, take the escalator up to the bridge, which dangled over the road below and led into the hospital. I would ride the elevator to the neurology wing and enter her room . . . wondering . . . how would she be today? My father's expression would often reveal her state. And he was always there. He would sit in that room all day, every day. Before he retired, he drove there after work, but after, he spent his days there. On one occasion, when Mom was in the ICU and visiting hours were limited, Dad and

I hovered at her bedside. She wasn't aware of our presence. When the nurse asked us to leave, Dad and I drove to O'Connells Pub for hamburgers and a beer. The dark oak, windowless tavern seemed appropriate for our mood. Then we journeyed the short distance to the St. Louis Zoo to pass the time. It was cold outside, I remember. Dad smoked cigars at that time in his life. We strolled through the zoo grounds and approached the monkey house. Dad carefully laid his cigar on a post outside the entrance to preserve it for later. We laughed at this gesture, something to laugh about. He retrieved the cigar for a few more puffs, upon our exit. It's funny, the things we recall. The zoo was empty, barren, and drab, and Dad didn't say much, but we were there, together.

[Allison] 1989: <u>The Room</u>
Don't ever attempt it,
If possible, stay away from The Room.
It has no windows, and only one door.
You may not breathe your last breath of air there, you may only watch others.
Yes, it is meant to be good, to save a life,
But daylight is not even allowed.
Is that good?

ALLISON—November 26, 1989: Mom got out of intensive care yesterday but is still in the hospital. She wasn't home for Thanksgiving—obviously. I'm at the hospital with mom and she's <u>gone</u>—she's just talking about all these strange things over and over. I feel bad for dad—I think he's lonely. This is going to be a strange Christmas, especially if mom isn't better.

The porcelain angel by her side . . .

ALLISON—December 6, 1989: Mom is doing <u>so</u> good. Her memory is pretty good and she is doing so much. Her hands are pretty good too. Thanks God! I'm so happy!

ALLISON—December 13, 1989: I'm having mixed thoughts on the DEA—Dad really doesn't want me to do it. And I know it's <u>my</u> decision but he has given me some things to think about. I really will be <u>risking my life.</u> What do I want out of life?

ALLISON—December 15, 1989: Yay! Tomorrow dad is coming to look at an apartment with me—I found one yesterday that I really loved. I'll probably move in January. I'm so excited! I am so lucky, mom and dad are so generous, they want us to be happy. I hope I can be such a good parent!

1990

(My mother is fifty-five and I am twenty-three)

ALLISON—January 7, 1990: Tomorrow I will officially be <u>in</u> my apartment. I signed my lease on the 2nd and have been moving in all week. Tomorrow night will be my first night with all my stuff. It is 1990! Mom is in the hospital, but is doing pretty good and she'll be out probably Tuesday. She had an infection. I start [graduate school] classes Wednesday. I'm excited but nervous. Tomorrow I have to go for this pseudo interview for some research work.

I was hired for the job, as a research assistant at the University of Missouri–St. Louis. The project on which I worked studied residential burglary and through a streetwise, former "thug," the researchers were able to interview over 100 "active burglars." The interviews took place on the school campus and each individual was paid $25 cash for their interview. These offenders were not in the criminal justice system; they had yet to be "caught." So the research was quite intriguing and the subjects were often fearful the project was a sting. They were asked questions about the burglaries they had committed: Did they stake out the house? Plan their crime? How did they get in? How did they get out? What kinds of things did they take? They were never asked exact addresses where their crimes had occurred, so as to avoid being arrested for and charged with those offenses. Among other things, the research determined the number one deterrent to a burglar was the presence of a dog. Very few wanted to encounter a canine! The "thug" who had the street contacts was actually a former car thief. He had been shot in a drive-by shooting in north St. Louis and, as a result, was paralyzed from the waist down. After being destined to a future in a wheelchair, he decided to return to school, earn his degree, and straighten out his life. He and I shared the same office. Me, the young, white, naïve, college graduate, and he, the middle aged, black, streetwise, former car thief. How would these two souls manage to share an office, communicate, and prosper? The wheelchair. He lived in one, as did my mother, and once he knew we shared this common thread, we became friends and confidantes. I probably learned more from him about criminal justice than I had my entire college career, majoring in the subject. Looking back on those days, I realize how "green" I was and suspect he likely had a few good laughs at my expense.

ALLISON—January 16, 1990: I love my apartment! I haven't been lonely yet. I've been thinking about the state of our world today. The Berlin Wall has just fallen, Russians and Romanians are revolting and demanding democracy. The Bible talks of one government before the second coming. That used to seem impossible to me. I wouldn't doubt it one bit if God was preparing to destroy the earth, he is probably so disgusted with us and the way we live. . . . I'm going to New York Friday, I can't wait! . . . Mom is doing so good! We went to see "Steel Magnolias" yesterday, just the two of us. She loved it, she never gets to go to the movies. It was so fun—it was about 65 degrees yesterday. In January!

ALLISON—January 22, 1990: I'm on the plane home. We had a great weekend! Friday we got to our hotel about 2:30 and Christie was waiting for us. (Eastern Air lost our luggage till 4:00pm on Saturday!) The three of us [Lori, Christie and I, high school friends] went to Rockefeller Center to see David Letterman. They accidentally gave us 3 tickets so Christie got to go also! The show was so good and so neat to watch how it's all done! Then we got ready and ate dinner then we went to this bar, $15 to get in! Saturday we shopped in Greenwich Village and Soho and ate lunch at a neat café. Lori and I got our luggage— finally—yay! Then we went to "The Phantom of the Opera" which was excellent! The show was so wonderful, I loved it. Dinner at The Iguana and then off to Mars. Lots of people standing outside waiting to get in but we were on the guest list (thanks to Christie's friend) and just walked right in! (we're cool! Ha!) This place was extremely interesting! 4 or 5 floors with different types of music on every floor (Reggae on one, R&R on one, etc) There was a girl there dancing with jeans and a bra on. We all danced and drank. It cost $17 to get in here! Sunday we shopped. Fun! Fun! Then Lori and I went to Runyons for dinner and watched them tape Costas Coast to Coast; a radio show, Bob Costas interviewed Boomer Isiason and some other guy. Afterwards, Lori and I met Bob and talked to him for a few minutes. He was very friendly.

Lori was my best friend throughout high school and college, though we attended different universities. As teenagers, we loitered at the mall every Friday night, idolized the Go-Gos and passed notes in history class (the 1980s version of text messaging). We were lucky in the sense that we both came from families whose fathers worked hard and made decent money and neither of us wanted for much. Both of our fathers, however, had come from modest means and knew how to save and spend wisely. But when it came to their children, our fathers were extremely generous. I suspect my father's generosity was compounded by my mother's condition—one less thing for us to worry about. In hindsight, it was likely a disservice to me, because I could barely balance a budget when I moved out on my own. However, I'll never complain about not having to obsess over money while growing up. The New York getaway had been purchased by my father and Lori's dad at a fundraising event for multiple sclerosis. The trip included the flight, hotel, the *David Letterman* show, tickets to the Broadway musical, and Costas' radio program. Our dads bid on the vacation, for Lori and me during a live auction. It was a trip I will never forget and a present from my father that I can never repay.

ALLISON—March 22, 1990: Six days til my birthday! My job is going really well. I'm learning so much, not just about Criminology, but about people and life and society. Tomorrow the people from the National Institute of Justice (NIJ) are coming. I'm nervous but excited. I'll get to meet people that I studied about as an undergrad!

ALLISON—March 23, 1990: The first day of the NIJ site visit was great! It was so interesting to meet these people. Their knowledge on crime is amazing. This is definitely the field for me! Something I've realized in the past couple of days—I really feel I'm more interested in the offenders rather than the criminal justice system. I think I want to get my PhD—I know I do after today, true, it's a lot of work, but there will be so many opportunities available. I hope this is the direction God wants me to take.

ALLISON—March 27, 1990: Tomorrow is my 23rd birthday. It doesn't bother me to be a year older, but I do think about men a lot and how in the world I'm going to meet the right one! Tonight I went to mom and dad's for dinner. Mom was really weak, dad is gonna take her to the doc tomorrow and she may have to go into the hospital. I hope not, but I know it is less of a burden for dad if she's there. Of course, his preference would be to have her home and well!

ALLISON—April 4, 1990: Lori and I went to Casas [Mexican restaurant] tonight. I talked to this guy from my high school—he is so nice. I want him to call me. He kind of hinted at it, but we'll see. I suppose if he really wants to— he will.

ALLISON—April 8, 1990: I'm such a hypochondriac—every little pain or itch, I imagine that something is wrong with me! It is so stupid—surely I have better things to worry about! I think about mom and how often she feels bad, it makes me mad at myself for worrying about dumb things. Sometimes I miss mom and dad while I'm here at my apartment. I don't know how I'd live without them, they have helped me every step of the way in my life. I'm so excited! Carolyn is coming home this weekend. I can't wait! I haven't seen her since January!

ALLISON—April 9, 1990: Today Emily is 4. I was just reading my book of poems and thoughts. I wish I had the guts to try and get some of those poems published, but, they're so personal...

ALLISON—April 17, 1990: We had a pretty good Easter—mom has been really weak and went into the hospital today. It seems like I've gotten immune to being really upset, but it bothers me because I just <u>assume</u> that everything will be all right and back to normal in a couple of days, and I hate to think of mom just lying in there while I'm out here having a good time. Diana and the girls came yesterday—the girls cried and were so upset when Diana took mom to the hospital. I babysat them; we had a lot of fun, danced, went to the park and McDonalds. We also went to the Magic House this morning, they are so cute! Lori and I saw these guys at Casas the other night that went to our high school (Rob). They came and sat by us. Anyway, Lori and I got tickets to a hockey game next week and Lori thinks I should ask Rob. He said if we got tickets to call him and I think he'd say yes, but I'm so sick of going out with guys from high school! He was a year older, but still!

ALLISON—April 19, 1990: I ended up asking Rob to the Blues game. He sounds really excited. I think it will be fun—who cares if it's not a "Love Connection." Ha! We should have a good time.

The following year, this man became my husband.

Rob made me laugh. He had a self-deprecating sense of humor with which he could easily win over a crowd. When Rob was "on," he was the life of the party. He could tell a tale or explain an experience he'd had, and the room would be doubled over with laughter. He never boasted or inflated himself and had so many friends, I could hardly keep track. When we enjoyed their company, I was shy and reserved as they were equally funny. Many of Rob's friends had a quick wit and sharp tongue, so I often kept quiet, for fear of sounding silly or immature. Early on, Rob's and my arguments tended to stem from my insecurity, my inability to socialize or make small talk.

ALLISON—April 27, 1990: Mom is coming home from the hospital today— yay! Except yesterday I went to see her and she was totally hallucinating. She told me she thought she could walk and would I help her stand up. Right then I looked up to the Lord and asked for his help. I just didn't know what to do. I didn't want her to fall and get hurt. Now that I think about it, God really answered my prayer because as I decided to help mom, in walked our minister from church. So mom just asked him to pray for her to walk and she didn't really ask me to help her stand after he left.

Mom didn't come home today because she was in one of her "states" this afternoon. So, I'm gonna go see her tomorrow, I hope she's not being crazy.

ALLISON—May 8, 1990: It's amazing how you continue to learn about yourself through your life. It's weird to think that next year, five years or twenty years from now, I'll know things about myself that I don't know now. Or perhaps, they aren't new things you learn but things you realize as you change. I think I've changed. I think I'm not as "normal" as I thought I was. Diana and I talked about this and she said that when you're younger you try to be like everyone else, you try to fit in because you want to be liked. But as you get older you don't really feel those constraints. You feel more free to be unique and original—to be yourself and usually that isn't "normal." Who is "normal" anyway? And what's so interesting about being normal? So, I guess I've realized I'm a little odd.

ALLISON—May 9, 1990: A new journal! How exciting! I love this one, I think it is so pretty. I can't believe this is my 7th journal! I'm so glad I've done it. If I ever lost these journals or if they were ever stolen, I would be heartbroken. I guess I won't think about it.

ALLISON—May 10, 1990: Mom is doing <u>so great!</u> She is so alert and really talks well. She's so hopeful and talking about her plans. Her hands are working good and she just seems like "my mom"—the mom I remember. It is so fun to go over there and be with her because she's doing so good. I can't explain how exciting it is and it just puts me in such a good mood!

ALLISON—June 19, 1990: Today I interviewed my second female burglar. It was very interesting. She was 25 and has done well over 100 burglaries and lots of drugs. I asked her what other crimes she's done and she says, "well, shoplifting, auto theft and we were robbing this guy and we killed him." I, of course, do not know who the victim was or when it occurred, but it bothers me. What bothers me even more is that after she admitted that to me, I tried to hate her and I couldn't. I liked her! I talked to my boss about it. He said he doesn't know anyone who works with offenders that doesn't end up liking some of them. He said that though they may do monsterous things and you may hate what they do; they aren't monsters, they're people. And you come to like and enjoy their humanity.

ALLISON—June 21, 1990: My boss suggested I write my thesis on female burglars. It would be interesting. Not many people have actually spoken with active female burglars. But I haven't decided whether or not to write a thesis [or take an extra course]. I just can't decide what to do with my <u>life?!</u>

ALLISON—July 8, 1990: Mom is in the hospital—she went in Friday. She has a bladder infection. I hope she doesn't end up having to be in there for long. I feel so sorry for her. Sometimes I feel like I just push it out of my mind, and I hate myself for not thinking of her more. I feel terrible when I go out and have fun and she's stuck in there, just laying there. I mean how come she got dealt such a crappy deal?! How come she has to live like this?

When the doctors administered steroids, my mother grew stronger. Her voice became louder, her speech more prominent. She could manipulate her hands and was wide-eyed when we would visit her in the hospital. However, this treatment came with a price. Her mind often left the room. On one occasion, I remember going to visit, and as I walked in the hospital room, she acknowledged me and said, "Hi, Ali." I thought all was well until I tried to speak and she told me to be quiet. For the rest of our visit, she waved me off so she could listen to Jesus, who was apparently one of the contestants on *Wheel of Fortune.* Hmmm… On another visit, my mother was convinced that something from the ceiling might fall on me so I had to continually dart around the room. On one visit, I was Satan and she wouldn't speak to me. These were the most difficult times for me. Seeing her sick and weak was almost less disturbing than seeing her as someone other than herself. I think it must be how individuals feel when their elderly parents or loved ones suffer from Alzheimer's disease. The "not knowing" someone any longer, the inability to communicate as you once did. Even when Mom was weak and barely able to move her limbs, she could still tell me she loved me and I could tell her and she understood. She could express fear and emotion. Not that I wished her to struggle, but a drug-induced mind did not seem to be worth it. Eventually, the hallucinations disappeared and the prednisone would leave a strength she did not previously possess.

ALLISON—July 11, 1990: I went to see mom yesterday and she was doing really good. We had a great visit. I miss her. I love when she's doing good because we can talk and it's like old times. She understands and can talk to me like normal. But we had fun, hopefully she'll come home soon. She seems stronger too. . . . Sometimes it really excites me to think about getting married to Rob and other times, it scares me to death. I think about all the things I'd like to do in life. I don't want to just get married, stay in St. Louis, have an okay job and then be a housewife.

ALLISON—July 12, 1990: I had class tonight. It's so strange. There is a lady in my class that really reminds me of mom. I know it sounds weird but I look at her and I think, "that's what my mom would be like or that's how my mom would walk if she could walk." I'm almost mesmerized by her.

ALLISON—July 19, 1990: I've hardly had any time alone recently to write. I've just been going, going, going. It has been a very hectic and stressful July. It really bothers me that I'm so *impatient sometimes. I wonder if we can change things like that, this late in life, or if that will always be part of my personality.*

ALLISON—August 7, 1990: Sunday was so fun. Mom, dad, Carolyn and I went to church then drove out to Labadie, Missouri. It's about a half hour drive from here. We ate lunch at a place called Hunters Hollow. It was really good and very quaint. The restaurant and shops next door looked like old fashioned storefronts. There was an antique store, a bakery, tavern, a country shop and a wine tasting. It was like stepping into another century. The drive was beautiful and such cute old houses on the roadside. It was so quiet and peaceful. I'll bet it will be beautiful in the fall with the leaves changing colors. I love going places like that, away from civilization.

ALLISON—August 8, 1990: Last night Rob and I talked about our future. We said maybe we'd get married in 1992. I think too many people rush into marriage and then divorce sets in. I'm not *ever getting a divorce. I want my marriage to be for life.*

With Rob I learned to appreciate alternative music and Cardinals baseball. Rob taught me the significance of a pitching change in the middle of an inning. The culinary world and a passion for wine were introduced to me through Rob and his large Italian family. Rob was like no one I had ever dated. He called when he said he would and showed up on my doorstep at just the time he had promised. I felt I had finally met the man who would behave as my father had, if I were to get sick, if MS came calling. Rob would rise to the challenge. Wouldn't he?

ALLISON—November 8, 1990: Right now I'm in the airport, waiting to go to Tulsa and then tomorrow we [Diana, Carolyn, and I] go to Dallas! I'm so excited! I hope we have a lot of fun!

This was the first of many "Sisters Weekends," shared by Carolyn, Diana, and me. I can't believe they began in 1990 and still continue today. The three of us pick a city and then plan a weekend trip in that venue. We have tried to go every other year, but sometimes "life" prevents us from getting away together. Santa Fe, Chicago, Phoenix . . . just to name a few. In 2008 the sisters were joined by the nieces (Megan and Emily), and the five of us *did* New York City. And did we ever! More on that later.

ALLISON—November 12, 1990: Mom is in intensive care. So much has happened. Wednesday (11/7) Aunt Carol took mom to Target and mom fell out of her wheelchair in the van and broke her leg. We didn't know it was broken until Thursday afternoon when they came out and took xrays (I was already in Tulsa). They took her to Barnes in an ambulance and they put a pin in her knee (she broke her femur bone). Dad called us in Tulsa Thursday night and said that she didn't have pneumonia but she'd probably be in traction for quite awhile and that they may have to do surgery next week on her leg. We talked to him Friday from Dallas and he said he'd only call if anything new happened. Sunday when we got back to Diana's we called the hospital. Diana made the call and asked to be connected with mom's room. I just saw Diana's eyes get big and she said, "what?!" I knew something awful had happened. We finally got a hold of dad in ICU. Mom's red blood count was real low and she wasn't getting enough oxygen in her blood. Dad said he thought he'd almost lost her at one point, he said her eyes rolled back in her head and the nurse started yelling for all these doctors and nurses. They took mom's arm and one nurse said, "She still has a pulse." Dad said he was scared, I wish so bad I would have been here with him. I got home about 8pm last night. Dad picked me up and we talked. My father is the strongest man in the world and sometimes I'm not sure how he makes it through all these times. How does mom's body take it?

And that is the kind of person and father my dad is. He was experiencing, perhaps, one of the worst days of his life, yet he didn't call us in Dallas. He didn't want to ruin our fun sisters' trip. Selfless.

ALLISON—November 13, 1990: Well, I saw mom yesterday 4 times and once this morning. She doesn't look too good to me but the doctors seem to think she is doing better. She just has so many tubes hooked up to her and her leg has a pin (actually looks like a nail) in it and is in a sling. She knows who we are, she isn't really disoriented or anything, but she's just sleepy all the time and can barely talk. She said she loves us and I told her that we needed her and she better not give up. Carolyn drove home last night from KU to stay the week. I was so glad. Carolyn and I spent the night at mom and dad's last night. I think dad was glad to have us there so he wouldn't feel alone. We all 3 hugged before dad went to bed. These times really bring us closer. I get so angry and bitter at God, though, I know he is sad for mom too. It is so hard in times like this to see God's purpose and know that there is a reason for all of mom's suffering. It is so unfair that she has to go through this over and over. It is amazing that her body can take this much. I guess her will to live is just extremely strong. I just don't want her to give up the fight. Though my mom's body is frail and weak, she is the strongest woman I know.

The porcelain angel by her side. . .

ALLISON—November 20, 1990: Mom is doing so much better. She's out of intensive care but will probably have to stay in traction for a week to a week and a half more. I'm so thankful and Thanksgiving is a day away! Last Thursday was the Multiple Sclerosis Sports Banquet. It was so fun and we got a lot of autographs. Carolyn got really upset. She kept saying that most of the people there were just there for $$ and status and that they didn't understand what MS was really like. Carolyn is really growing up, sometimes I don't think I give her enough credit.

ALLISON—November 25, 1990: I had a wonderful Thanksgiving weekend! Us girls took turkey dinner to mom at the hospital. Friday, mom came home! She has a cast on her leg though. But she's doing so good. She was kind of depressed on Saturday because she feels like she's a hassle but I think she cheered up today.

Saturday, Diana, Carolyn, Megan and Emily and I baked cookies and just messed around. That night we all played games.

ALLISON—December 22, 1990: ROB PROPOSED!!

ALLISON—December 24, 1990: It is Christmas Eve. Tonight Rob and I will tell our families that we're engaged. I'm so excited, nervous, scared and happy. I hope mom and dad are excited. I think mom and dad will be totally shocked.

ALLISON—December 29, 1990: Mom, dad and Carolyn were so excited! We all started hugging and we opened champagne. They were all three shocked and they all cried (even dad). It was so fun! And they were so happy for us. Christmas night Diana and Steve and the kids got here. Right before we opened gifts dad brought in a bottle of champagne and said that Rob and I had something to tell them. Diana turned around and looked at me and her mouth dropped open. Once we told them everyone got excited and Megan and Emily were asking what was going on. We told them there was going to be a wedding and the girls were ecstatic!

1991

(My mother is fifty-six and I am twenty-four)

ALLISON—January 1, 1991: I'm so excited about our wedding, getting ready and all but I wish mom felt better. She's pretty weak and so upset about the cast. I want to include her in our plans, I wish so badly she and I could go look at wedding dresses together. I know she wants to too. Mom has been so depressed this whole holiday season. I know it's because of the cast but I just don't want her to give up.

ALLISON—January 14, 1991: Tomorrow we will find out if the United States is going to war with Saudi Arabia. We are trying to defend a little country (Kuwait) and our oil, Sadam Husein (maniac) has invaded Kuwait and if he isn't out by midnight, January 15, we will declare war. It is so scary. Our soldiers have been there since August. People around town have yellow ribbons around their trees meaning they have a loved one over there. I have never experienced something so close to war in my lifetime. At times you can forget and say, well Saudi Arabia is so far away, but supposedly Husein has terrorists ready to murder Americans in the U.S. Carolyn and I wrote letters to "any service member" and sent them. We just let them know how much we appreciate what they're doing and tell them we won't forget about them. I am in the cafeteria at school and I can hear 2 people talking about the possible war right now.

Obviously, my knowledge of the Middle East was slim. I was quite surprised when I returned to this journal and read the war "play by play" I had extracted from watching the nightly news.

ALLISON—January 16, 1991: It is 6pm here but 3am in Saudi Arabia. They are saying that the U.S. has begun some kind of an attack on Iraq.

ALLISON—January 20, 1991: Yes, we are at war with Iraq. Those first two days (1/16 and 1/17) we watched TV nonstop. The U.S. made an air attack on Bagdad and other parts of Iraq, which continues today. Iraq barely fought back in the beginning. Then Thursday night they attacked Israel. Iraq began to bomb Saudi Arabia as well. We are doing a lot of damage. Iraq has been firing "SCUD" missiles.

This seems to be their only weapon. We have captured some Iraq POWs, but they have some of our men as well. So far we've lost 15 planes. It is so scary. Iraq isn't backing down as it was first thought they would. It is so strange how this is happening. There are a lot of protestors in this country. But, I believe there are more Americans who support our president than those who don't.

ALLISON—January 30, 1991: The war is still going on. There have been so many attacks on Israel and today we may have lost our first ground troops. Sadam opened some oil tank pipes into the Persian Gulf. There is a huge oil slick in those waters now, it is a disaster, they say. Sadam is Hitler all over again. I think George Bush is doing a really good job, I would hate to be in his shoes right now. The war isn't on TV as much now but people are still talking about it all the time. Our world is so uncertain right now, well, always.

ALLISON—February 12, 1991: Mom had a wonderful birthday Saturday. Diana, Steve, Megan, Emily and Carolyn were in town. Diana and the girls and I took mom to see my wedding dress. We had Pasta House for dinner and after dinner we watched old home movies and laughed so hard! It was so fun! Mom is doing great! She was up the whole day. Mom, dad, Carolyn and I are going to Sarasota in March! I'm so excited!

ALLISON—February 25, 1991: Yesterday the ground war began and the Iraqi troops are surrendering by the 1000s. A lot of people think the war will end soon, maybe even in a few days, but I don't know. . . . I'm scared to start looking for a job. I'm so bad in interviews, I think. And I hate them, but I suppose you can't get a job without one. . . . I can't wait to marry Rob but I want to have a good job and stuff also. I just want to feel productive, I want to feel like I'm making a difference.

ALLISON—March 7, 1991: The war ended last week! We got most of our POWs back and troops are going to begin coming home soon. It is very exciting! I can't wait for the parade! Sadam's troops couldn't come close to handling us in the ground war. We were much too skilled and powerful. I guess our government has done something worthwhile with all that defense money. I feel very safe to be an American. . . . We go to Florida Saturday (mom, dad, Carolyn and I). I'm so excited but it is kind of sad, our last trip just the 4 of us.

ALLISON—March 13, 1991: I'm sitting on our balcony, looking at the gulf of Mexico, listening to the surf hit the shore. It is fairly cloudy and windy, but warm.

I'm really having a good time. Carolyn and I have been able to spend a lot of time together, talking and stuff. . . . I've been looking for a new job. I'm getting nervous that I'm not going to find anything (in my field). I want to find something that pays well so I'll be able to contribute to our marriage.

ALLISON—April 4, 1991: Mom got the brace off of her leg, however, her leg isn't healed. The doctor said it probably wouldn't heal without surgery and even then it isn't guaranteed. He said it would be fine as long as she didn't put any weight on it, which she can't anyway. Dad said to me, "I don't want her to give up hope of walking—but I don't think she's ever going to walk again." It was strange to hear him say that, tho I know that is what he's been thinking. I'm not sure what to think, is it unrealistic to think she'll walk again? Miracles do happen and mom is so determined. Sunday Rob and I are doing a walk-a-thon for M.S. It is going to be hard—12 miles, but I just have to remember what mom and all the people with M.S. would give if they could walk, and I'm so lucky that I can!

ALLISON—April 7, 1991: My feet hurt! Just kidding! Today was our walk, it was so fun. I wasn't really tired til the last mile.

ALLISON—April 15, 1991: I had a great weekend—except, mom had to go in the hospital with pneumonia. But she's in good spirits and seems to be doing pretty good. It's amazing how I've gotten so used to it, hearing messages from dad that mom has been taken to the hospital. It is just a part of our life. . . . Mom is so cool. I went to the hospital right after she was admitted. A nurse came in to ask mom a bunch of questions on mom's history. Mom was so sweet and funny and she made the nurse laugh. Mom has a good sense of humor, something I tend to forget. It is strange to see your parents around others or their peers—you really respect and appreciate them. The nurse seemed really surprised that mom looked so good and was doing so well after 20 years of M.S. She told mom, "you've got a good sense of humor, and your spirit and that's what's important." People really like mom.

ALLISON—May 7, 1991: Mom is in the hospital again. She is just so weak. Hopefully an IV will help. I get scared sometimes that something will happen to her before our wedding. God just has to help her keep fighting.

ALLISON—May 21, 1991: Mom came home from the hospital Friday but dad put her back in last night. She just doesn't seem to be getting stronger, or she seems strong in the hospital and then very weak when she gets home. Dr. Trotter thought she should come into Barnes downtown instead of West County so that's where she is now. Hasn't she been thru enough! It seems so unfair sometimes. I know that when bad things happen to good people it is to glorify God, but that is hard to realize and understand when it's your mother.

ALLISON—June 4, 1991: Tonight I'm in Jefferson City [Missouri]. Tomorrow is my interview with Probation & Parole. I'm nervous, but want to get it over with. I need a job, any job. I'm in the hotel bar now. I hope none of my interviewers are here! I really enjoy this time alone. I love going new places, this hotel is so cool. . . . I guess Grandma Redfern isn't doing so great with her battle with cancer. I wish I could see her, I feel bad about that. She must be frightened and scared. . . . Mom is home and doing so good. She is stronger and so with it. She's so fun to talk to. It is sad in a way tho, because I wish she would stay this way forever. The disease goes so back and forth that I know she'll have a relapse. I'm just trying to enjoy it while she's doing good. She's just like my "mom" that I grew up with.

ALLISON—June 25, 1991: I'm out of my apartment. I moved out Sunday. I'm kind of glad to be home. I'm still worried about jobs.

Later in the month of June 1991, I received the letter advising I had been hired as a Missouri Probation and Parole Officer. I was going to earn $18,000 per year! That sounded amazing! I would be making more than $1,000 a month! I had never held a full-time job and was already spending the income in my mind. My first day on the job was July 15, 1991, and initially, I worked as a supervision officer. After an offender had been placed on probation or upon their release from prison, onto parole, they were assigned to my caseload. They were required to report to my office monthly, and I was responsible for ensuring they were abiding by the conditions of their supervision. If an offender violated their term of supervision, I was required to report the violation to the court or parole board. The judge or parole commissioner would then decide whether to issue a warrant for their arrest or continue their supervision term. The more interesting days were those when a warrant had been issued and the offender reported to the office for their monthly meeting. Before walking them back to my office, I would telephone the St. Louis City Police and advise that the offender had reported as scheduled. The office visit would commence, and I would attempt to prolong our conversation until the police arrived. The officers would enter my cubicle and place my "client" in handcuffs, arresting them on the violator's warrant. On a few occasions, we had "runners." As soon as they saw the uniformed police officers, they took off running through the Probation Office. Usually they were tackled before they made it to the street, but if not, then a few blocks away.

Individuals on state probation or parole in St. Louis city exist in desperate life circumstances. Many have little, if any, income, no education, and limited employment history. A good percentage are drug users with very little future. Most of their situations seem so hopeless. Many of those on supervision had parents on supervision, and therefore, probably never had a chance. Their crimes range from drug sales, burglary, robbery, theft, and/or rape, to murder. After two years, I transferred to the presentence investigation unit. In this unit, I was assigned a case after the individual had pled guilty but before they were sentenced. It was my duty to interview the offender, conduct a thorough background check and prepare a report for the sentencing judge. The presentence investigation report included a synopsis of the crime the offender had committed; their criminal history; information about their upbringing, such as family, education, employment, mental health, and substance abuse; and, finally, a recommendation to the judge on the sentence the offender should receive. I interviewed car thieves, drug dealers, armed robbers, men who had killed their wives, and child molesters. You name it, I've heard it. I worked in this capacity for six more years.

ALLISON—July 29, 1991: Yesterday we drove up to visit Grama Redfern. She seemed really depressed and looked old. She cried and told us she was scared and close to giving up. I've never seen her cry. Her cancer is back and I don't think they're really doing any treatment now. I think it really helped her to talk to mom. Mom could talk to her because she knows how it feels to wake up and feel sick and want to feel well. Dad is worried, I can tell.

ALLISON—August 13, 1991: Grama is in the hospital in Springfield. Dad has been going up to visit her. Dad said he doesn't think she'll make it more than a couple of weeks. It's strange. Grama will be the first person in my life (that I've known well) to pass away. That's very rare, being 24.

ALLISON—August 15, 1991: Grandma Redfern died last night. Yesterday, mom and dad went up to see her because grandpa said he wasn't sure if she'd make it thru the day. Mom and dad came home and then Uncle Larry called about 12:30am and said she died about 12:15am. Dad came in my room and told me. I cried last night, a lot when I got into bed. And I just feel sick to my stomach. I keep thinking about where she is now and what it must be like. . . . I feel so bad for dad, Grandpa and Uncle Larry. Dad was sad last night. I'm sure he's remembering growing up and Grama raising him from a little boy. And Grandpa, they were married 60 years last year. I'm sure he must be lonely and wondering what he's gonna do now by himself. The funeral is Saturday.

ALLISON—August 26, 1991: Grama's funeral was sad. I guess funerals usually are, but it was my first (except Great Grama Lorton). The visitation was the worst, seeing all those people and we were there for 4 hours with the casket open. I kept looking at Grandpa and imagining 61 years they had together. The funeral wasn't so bad, it was almost comforting thinking about Grama in heaven. But when they closed the casket, that was awful. Aunt Susie gave me a tablecloth Grama had embroidered, what a wonderful keepsake. . . . Mom hasn't been feeling too good lately. I hope she's just tired. It scares me to think mom might not be doing good at the wedding. Dad is out of town tonight and tomorrow which makes it worse.

ALLISON—September 5, 1991: 51 days!!! I can't believe it! I had a long talk with mom the other night. She wants to be more a part of the wedding plans. She feels like she has no idea what's going on. I feel bad because I know I've done so much on my own and not included her. I've got to try harder to make her more a part of it all.

ALLISON—September 12, 1991: Mom is doing really good and we're going to meet with the organist tonight and then meeting dad for dinner. I'm so excited!

ALLISON—October 13, 1991: 13 days til our wedding! I can't believe how close it is! The rehearsal dinner is pretty much finalized, so is the reception, the band, the limo, the programs are in. I got my portrait done Saturday and my dress is here now! Mom has been in the hospital this past week but she came home today—thank God! Next Saturday is my bachelorette party! I'm so excited, I can't believe it's all really happening. I've been waiting all my life for this day!!

ALLISON—November 6, 1991: Well, it's all happened! Everything was so wonderful! It may take me awhile to write it all, but I'll try . . .

ALLISON—December 16, 1991: Something awful happened this weekend. We had to put Pepper to sleep. The vet said he had a big tumor on his liver or spleen. Pepper hadn't eaten for 3 days. He was 13 years old and he was having trouble getting around. It was so sad. I keep thinking about him. I know it was best because he didn't seem happy anymore, but it's just so awful that we had to put him to sleep. I wish so badly that he had died by himself in his sleep or something. I felt like we were betraying him by putting him down. I know it sounds silly. . . . Over Thanksgiving, Carolyn, dad and I went to Grandma's grave. It was so strange. I keep thinking about dad and what a loss he must feel. Death is so awful, so unknown. I hate thinking about it.

ALLISON—December 20, 1991: I can't wait for Christmas! Carolyn and I went to the "Nutcracker" last night and to dinner. We had so much fun but talked about Pepper at dinner and got sad. The show was so good. It really makes me wish I had been good enough to be a dancer.

[Jane] Date Unknown: <u>An Ode to My Dog, Pepper</u>
For thirteen years you were a faithful friend
That must be why I loved you so.
Some time has passed but still I miss you.
I'm sure that you must know.
So much help you were to me.
If I needed help you would run
You would bark and bark to let them know.
Then soon somebody would come.
When we had been out and got back home
You would meet us at the door
You were so glad to see us
Oh, but I miss how things were before.
The fact that you were just a mutt,
It made no difference to me.
You were here when I needed you most.
That's how it was meant to be.
Times I wish you could have been here longer..
It just doesn't seem fair.
Some people say there's a doggie heaven
Somehow I know you are there.

1992

(My mother is fifty-seven and I am twenty-five)

ALLISON—January 7, 1992: It's 1992! Christmas was sort of a let down this year. I got into an argument with mom and dad. I think I was upset because of the fact that my parents are getting older. They both have so much trouble remembering things. I don't want my parents to get old and it scares me. Sometimes I wish I were more grown up. I'm so selfish sometimes. I was so depressed with work yesterday. Our office is so poorly run and yesterday was so hectic and frustrating. I do like my job, but sometimes I wish I was going to work with normal clients and not criminals. I don't really know what I want to do. Well, yes I do. I really want to write and publish my works. I'm not really sure how to go about it. That really is my dream, what a life!

ALLISON—March 9, 1992: Rob and I got a puppy—his name is Sidney. We've had him 3 weeks. He's so cute but sure has changed our lives!

ALLISON—May 7, 1992: So much has happened. Dad retired 3/31, mom went into intensive care the same day. She was on a respirator for 2 ½ weeks and the doctors were worried. She was in the hospital 3 ½ weeks, but she's home and doing great! Rob and I bought a house! The final contract was signed May 5, we close June 19 and move in then! Tomorrow we're going to KC for Carolyn's graduation, which is Sunday. I'm so excited to go and so happy for her. We get to stay at a hotel and we're going on the plaza for dinner Saturday.

Rob and I purchased our first home, a ranch-style house in a nice, conservative neighborhood in west St. Louis County in 1992. We house hunted for one day and signed a contract that night. Children and baby strollers swarmed the sidewalks. We were positioning ourselves for the American dream . . . a mortgage, two cars, two jobs, two kids, a dog . . . boredom. If I held that feeling subconsciously, I didn't fight it and let these events unfold until my life was moving on a course I was not actually, actively choosing. This was just how it was supposed to be for a young woman, right? I would learn to cook and clean and in a few years, get pregnant and that would be it. I bought in. But I was restless. That restlessness likely contributed to the issues Rob and I began facing. I wasn't content. But this was how my grandmother, my mother, and sister had lived, were living, and they each seemed happy and satisfied with their life's path. What was wrong with me?

ALLISON—July 1, 1992: We are in our house and loving it! I guess it will just take awhile til it feels like our "home." We're having fun decorating and fixing it up. I can't believe we own a home! Sometimes I miss being alone. It seems like the only time I'm alone is when I'm driving to and from work. I used to go places by myself and do interesting things like the art museum, etc. I guess I need to make more of an effort. I'm also lacking in my writing and poetry and reading and just looking ahead toward the future. It sometimes seems as if I'm in a rut, just doing 8-5, doing chores and going to bed. I want to use my mind and I don't want my job to be my life, at least not this job! I need to be more creative. I just need to take the time and put some effort into the things I enjoy. I don't mean for this to sound like I'm unhappy—I'm not at all, I'm just unfocused. It is so strange how I'm continually changing. I used to think—I'm set—I know exactly who I am and what I want and then . . . I'm different. I used to think I was such an individual that I was wild and not at all domestic. Now, I love cooking and I want to plant flowers! I'm not ready for children. I love my freedom. I do hope that feeling changes eventually. I want to have kids someday.

ALLISON—July 29, 1992: Carolyn comes home Friday for good. She's done with college! I can't wait for her to come home but I'm sure she's not too excited.

ALLISON—September 30, 1992: Carolyn, Diana and I nominated mom for "M.S. Mother of the Year" this summer. The Society called her yesterday and told her she won! There is a banquet and she'll receive an award on October 17. Mom is so excited. Carolyn said mom couldn't stop talking about it last night!

October 17 arrived and mom was hospitalized. I didn't make a journal entry but I recall she was heartbroken that she had to miss her ceremony. Diana, Carolyn, and I attended the banquet and accepted the award on her behalf, but once again, she had missed out on an event and life wasn't fair.

ALLISON—November 3, 1992: Today is election day. Bush, Clinton, Perot.

1993

(My mother is fifty-eight and I am twenty-six)

ALLISON—January 15, 1993: Over two months since I've written! It's 1993—so far this year has been great. Clinton won the election. The inauguration is next week. I hope he'll be a good president. The Democrats took over the election. We had a great holiday season. Christmas was wonderful with our families. Mom wasn't doing too well though and had to go in ICU on 12/30/92. She's still in the hospital but out of ICU now. Grandpa Rolston [my mother's father] had a stroke in November and had to go in a nursing home for a couple weeks. He's home now but not doing too great I don't think.

ALLISON—March 24, 1993: I realize I'm not near as good at writing anymore. So much has happened. Grandpa Rolston died 2-17-93. It was so sad, I didn't expect it really. We all went to Franklin for the weekend. All the cousins got to be there. It was really good to see everyone. Grandpa was such a good man and I'm so lucky to have the book he wrote to show my grandchildren and children. Uncle Ed read a poem I wrote for grandpa at the funeral. I had written it when I was a teenager. I was so surprised that he read it, but it made me feel good. I feel so bad for grandma. She must be so lonely—I can't imagine after 65 years of marriage, what a loss that must be. Just always having that person there and then they're gone. Something I really realized at grandpa's funeral is that the body is just a shell, it doesn't say who we are. I kept looking at grandpa's body but knew it wasn't "him." "He" is in heaven and the body is useless now. Mom is doing ok. She's home and has recently been having a lot of hallucinations. I think we're all afraid that the M.S. is affecting her mind. She has a feeding tube in her stomach now—dad was nervous, I think, to ok it. Dad isn't doing too great either. He just looks tired and run down. Hopefully, with spring almost here it will help. Then he can get out and play golf.

ALLISON—April 24, 1993: Grandma Rolston was here for Easter. It was so good to see her. She said she's been lonely and sometimes thinks she hears Grandpa. I feel bad for her, the loss must be so great. She really is a strong woman. She gave dad Grandpa's diamond wedding ring. She said she thought dad had "certainly earned it." I think dad was really honored.

My mother's parents were wonderful, loving Methodists. They lived their lives as pure and spiritual as I can imagine is possible. They had been married for sixty-six years when my grandfather died. Though they had a son, my grandmother gave that wedding ring to my father because of how he had cared for my mother through the years. They were always thankful their daughter had chosen the husband she did, as many marriages end after an MS diagnosis.

1994

(My mother is fifty-nine and I am twenty-seven)

ALLISON—May 17, 1994: I've been thinking a lot about having a baby. Rob would love to now. I know I'm not ready now but will I be ready next year? or the next? I can't tell Rob this because he is so eager. I want to give him a baby but I'm so scared of the whole thing. Our lives will change <u>forever</u>, we will be responsible for that child forever.

Rob and I tried for several years to conceive with no luck. As we struggled through that time, it was devastating. Despite that entry in 1994, I came to believe I wanted a child, and each month sent me into a deeper despair. Those who have not experienced it cannot understand, just as I didn't before it was happening to me. You question your body, your husband's body, and you wonder why they are not functioning properly, together. We were both healthy, young, and felt we could provide a good home for a child. Yet, I was working in a field where crack-addicted, unmarried women were getting pregnant and regretting the choices they had made. Of course, being of childbearing age, my friends were conceiving and sharing their joyous news. I smiled and feigned happiness for them, but each announcement felt like a harsh slap in the face.

1995

(My mother is sixty and I am twenty-eight)

ALLISON—May 3, 1995: It has been two weeks since the Oklahoma City bombing. It happened on a Wednesday—April 19, 1995. I've been saving all the newspaper clippings. It was so horrifying. I remember when Rob called me at work and said the federal building in Oklahoma City had been bombed. All we knew was that there were 300-500 people that worked there and it was believed that Iranian terrorists had done it. Well, so far, the death toll is @ 140 with 30-40 people still missing. They have arrested one guy and charged him—Timothy McVeigh. I watched the first news clips and the Memorial service with Clinton and Rev. Billy Graham. It was so sad, I cried a lot. 15 children were murdered, they were in the building at a daycare. All those people, just going to work for a regular day, not knowing it would be their last day on earth, how strange.

ALLISON—November 28, 1995: Mom is in the hospital with pneumonia— she's not doing well. I saw her today and she would not eat, she wasn't herself, she was kind of stubborn and angry. I know she's frustrated. Dad called tonight and said the doc said the pneumonia is much worse. Her oxygen was real low too.

The porcelain angel by her side . . .

The doctor asked dad if mom doesn't get better in a few days or so, does he want to put her on a ventilator. Dad said yes. He told me he will try it but he doesn't want her to keep suffering. I asked what if they don't do the ventilator and he said, "She'll die." I'm so lost. I don't want to lose my mother yet. I really wanted her to see me have a baby. Yesterday mom was looking at the ceiling and we asked what she was looking at, she said, "heaven." I'm so afraid that's true. I'm just being selfish because I don't want her to go yet. I wonder if God wants her now. . . . I know I've seen her worse but she was younger and a body can only take so much. I'm trying to be positive though. . . . Last week two girls from my office, Kathleen and Angela, were killed in a car accident. Kathleen was 30 and Angie was 26. It was just awful, so tragic. It really made me think, life is so precious. That Friday before, Angie was the last person I said bye to before I left. She said, "have a good weekend!" and I said, "you too!" Then Saturday, she died. It is still so weird to me. She was in the office next to me. I've never had someone my age that I know, die. The only funerals I've been to are my grandparents and a friend's dad. It's really strange to think they're gone. I can't imagine how the families must feel. To have someone taken so quickly and sudden. Needless to say, the past 2 weeks have been so depressing.

1996

(My mother is sixty-one and I am twenty-nine)

In March of 1996, our entire family took a vacation to Sarasota. Rob and I drove to Florida with my parents, which was an experience in and of itself. We stopped in Georgia and all shared a motel room. I suppose Rob and I were too poor to spring for our own room, but we paid for it in lack of sleep. Both of my parents snored, and neither had learned the definition of "whisper" once the lights were extinguished. Dad continues to suffer from "loud voice," especially at the cinema. It's ironic, because he is a quiet man, who, as I mentioned, never shouts. He just hasn't established a "movie theater tone" or "those people at the next table can hear what you are saying about them" voice. And so, I digress. Once we arrived on the gulf, Mom was able to enjoy the pool and beach, and we made many wonderful memories. We still laugh at our game of Charades when hotel security was called to a "spring breakers bash" only to discover my parents, sisters, and young nieces in our pajamas, and Dad insisting that *Bewitched* was a three-syllable television show. My father's Charades technique is as follows: his "clues" are limited to the twirling of his index finger, as in "you're close, keep guessing." But he offers nothing more. During the week, we visited our favorite restaurants, developed our suntans and cheered the Cardinals as they played a spring training game against the Pittsburgh Pirates (Cardinals won!) This would be my mother's last trip to her favorite place.

During 1996, Rob and I underwent various tests and procedures and yet the doctors could not find a cause or reason we were not able to conceive. I remember becoming angry with my mother on one occasion when she told me I just needed to relax. I was taking my temperature daily, having blood drawn every week, and anticipating the outcome every month. How could one relax!? The local news ran a story about a woman who left her newborn in a dumpster because she'd already given birth to seven children. Anger. One fertility specialist suggested a procedure to us that would cost $4,000. If I didn't become pregnant, obviously it would be as though we had burned the money. Rob and I argued over our grocery bills, so I wasn't sure how we were going to scrape up that kind of cash. I knew my parents and his parents would help, but I couldn't imagine the devastation and guilt (and debt) we would feel, if it didn't work. I could not understand why we had to experience such turmoil, and meanwhile the stress was having its affect on our marriage.

1997

(My mother is sixty-two and I am thirty)

ALLISON—June 4, 1997: Carolyn got into SLU [St. Louis University] law school! I'm so happy for her! I'm so glad she decided to GO FOR IT. . . . I was just reading thru this journal and saw that I had written about the day of the Oklahoma City bombing. On Monday McVeigh was found guilty on all federal charges. Now they are deciding the penalty. . . . Turning 30 was easy. I did reflect on the last decade and how different my life is at 30 than it was at 20.

ALLISON—September 7, 1997: On Sunday morning (8-31-97) Princess Diana was killed in a car accident. It was so sad. I was watching CNN in Kansas City when they announced it. She was with her boyfriend and they have since learned that the car's driver was drunk and they were being chased by paparazzi. The funeral was yesterday and it was so depressing. She was so involved in charity— so elegant and young (36).

Rob and I maintained a romantic relationship through the years. Intimacy, however, had managed to escape and rarely returned for a visit. Our arguments grew more frequent, and more hateful. I often shared my growing unhappiness and disappointment with Carolyn, but to the rest of our circle, our marriage appeared to be fun-loving and stable.

1998

(My mother is sixty-three and I am thirty-one)

In May of 1998, Rob and I hosted a barbeque for some friends. We entertained quite a bit in those days. It was always a party when our close friends joined us on our large deck. We grilled steaks or hot dogs and drank wine and beer to the wee hours of the morning. At this particular barbeque, we served, among other things, corn on the cob. I love corn on the cob . . . dripping with butter, generously seasoned with salt, yum. When I was younger, maybe ten or twelve, Carolyn, my cousin Debbie, and I went to visit my grandparents, and the girls dared me to see how many ears of corn I could eat. Of course, my grandmother got her corn fresh from the farm, and there is nothing quite like the taste of sweet corn from Illinois. So, back to our party . . . as the wine and beer were consumed and the trash began to overflow, a corn cob was tossed onto the load, teetering just off the edge. Our dog, Sidney, the canine garbage disposal, quickly nabbed and swallowed the cob before anyone could stop the violation. We were concerned, but he seemed fine, and so the party continued with our usual tales and laughter. Over the next few days, Sidney ate but was not able to keep food in his stomach. A trip to the vet confirmed our fears, the cob was blocking the passageway to his digestive system. With surgery, he would be fine. Without it, he would die. The surgery, $1,000, was not an expense Rob and I had saved for, but we had no choice as we loved that dog. After many tears and days of stress, Sidney pulled through and adopted the nickname, the "corn cob dog" at our local veterinary clinic. The vet even offered us the undigested corn cob stored in a plastic baggie, as a keepsake. No thanks.

In July of 1998, my grandmother, my aunts, and my female cousins drove to St. Louis for a family reunion. All seventeen of us stayed at my parents' house, sleeping on floors and in campers. It was a joyous occasion for my mother, just laughing with her sisters. We had goofy T-shirts emblazoned with "Rolston Reunion" made for each family member and modeled them for photos. We grilled bratwursts, swam, played Dutch Blitz, and reminisced about our childhood days. It is an event I am so thankful we planned, not knowing how the next years would unfold.

ALLISON—Mom spent October '98 in the hospital. She got pretty bad and I think we almost lost her. One night dad called the nurse to see how mom was sleeping and the nurse said something like, "she's very ill but she's going to be going to a better place." Dad freaked out, I think, though dad doesn't really "freak out." He just said he couldn't sleep. Mom pulled thru but her mind was wacko for awhile. She wouldn't even talk to me when she got home. It was so strange.

1999

(My mother is sixty-four and I am thirty-two)

ALLISON—February 16, 1999: Carolyn is doing really well in law school and we have become so close. We see each other a lot and get along so well. In March, Diana, Carolyn and I are going to Sante Fe!!! I'm so excited, we have such fun things planned.

ALLISON—February 19, 1999: Dad took mom to the hospital today. She has a bladder infection and pneumonia. I can tell he's worried. Each time she's weaker and we all know one of these times she won't be strong enough to fight anymore. I'm numb. I keep trying to prepare myself, to think about death, so it won't be so awful— but it's all a lie and I know it. No one can really be prepared. I want mom to be okay but I want her to be happy and to be able to enjoy things. There are so many things I still want to share with my mother, I want her to hold my baby someday and I really don't see that happening. Life is so unfair. But mom still has hope of walking someday—how ironic.

On March 4, 1999, Diana, Carolyn, and I arrived in New Mexico for another "Sisters' Weekend!" We each purchased a roundtrip ticket for the "Shuttle Jack," which would safely transport us from Albuquerque to Santa Fe. Safety, however, was apparently not in the van service contract. The shuttle driver veered off the road more often than not and on several occasions, appeared to be dozing at the wheel. One passenger brutally scolded him. Luckily, we finally arrived in Santa Fe unscathed, but we learned from the local newspaper that the business folded the following day! Carolyn, Diana, and I spent three days dining on local culinary delights and shopping on Palace Avenue. We enjoyed a wonderful afternoon at Ten Thousand Waves Spa. The Japanese health spa nestled in the mountain basin was adorned with lush foliage, oriental lanterns, and wooden-planked huts. We were offered oatmeal-colored kimonos and given our own outdoor private hot tub for one hour. Off to the massage tables . . . so relaxing, so wonderful, so naked! That evening, we stumbled upon a Spanish wine tasting at La Casa Sena, complete with tapenade and toast points, smoked cheese, and grilled shrimp. We each sought out wine glasses at the company store etched with the south-of-the-border name. Thirteen years later, when I treat my La Casa Sena glass to a rich Malbec, I reminisce about that Santa Fe experience with my sisters.

ALLISON—April 27, 1999: The most awful thing happened a week ago today (4-20-99). Two teenage boys shot 12 kids and a teacher at their school in Colorado. They brought in @ 50 bombs and probably planned on doing a lot more harm and damage. They shot kids as they pleaded for their lives. They asked a girl if she believed in God and she said yes so they shot her in the head. They apparently worshipped Hitler (it was the anniversary of his birthday) and had planned their attack for a year. They killed themselves in the school so of course, there are so many unanswered questions. The news reports . . . it's just unfathomable to see kids running from their school in horror. . . . Last night Rob and I had a brief discussion about having a baby, or should I say, not having a baby. I think we are both so disheartened by this Colorado shooting and just the state of our world that we can't imagine bringing a child into the world. I think we both want to wait and travel and see if we feel differently in a few years. . . . I'm applying with the Feds again. I'm in limbo, waiting to hear something.

ALLISON—May 27, 1999: I don't want to stay at my current job for the rest of my life. I enjoy it but I want a new challenge! . . . Mom just got out of the hospital last week after 2 ½ weeks—very stressful. I thought she was going to die, I think that every time now. One day I was visiting alone and she was on the ventilator and looked so sick and pathetic. I said, "mom, don't give up" and a little tear rolled down her face. I felt bad, like she keeps fighting so as not to let us down.

The porcelain angel by her side . . .

In 1999, after several bouts of pneumonia, the doctors encouraged my mother to have a tracheotomy. As such, her lungs could be suctioned to prevent fluid buildup. One of the issues she was facing was aspiration. Food or food particles were making their way into her lungs, causing infection. I am not a medical professional, but this is how I understood the problem. This was not an easy decision for my parents. In addition to the tracheotomy, a tube would be placed in her stomach, and that is how she would be fed. Our family loves food. My sisters and I love to cook (though this didn't develop for me until my later years; Kraft macaroni and cheese was about all I could prepare as a teenager), and eating together was always a family affair. I remember my mother grieving at the thought of no longer being able to enjoy food. But my parents soon realized this probably was her only option. Once she had the procedures, our family events changed. At first, she sat with us during family dinners, but soon realized the smells and aromas of the meals were too much to bear. So, she resorted to staying in her bedroom while we dined together, though we did this less often. For Mother's Day, which is often a day filled with brunches or dinners, we decided to spend the afternoon at the St. Louis Art Museum, a celebration that did not revolve around food. I will always remember that day, as it was different from any other Mother's Day we had enjoyed, and it was joyous. I had no way of knowing it would be her last.

ALLISON—July 24, 1999: I haven't shared this with anyone but sometimes I'm afraid something is wrong with me, physically. I'm so clumsy sometimes, I drop things and knock things over. I've even noticed that there are times I stumble over words, like my mouth is full of marbles. Almost every morning I wake up and one of my arms feels like it's still asleep. I don't want to have M.S. It scares me so.

In July 1999, I left my office and walked down the hall to speak with a coworker. When I returned, I had a voice mail message from the chief U.S. probation officer in the Eastern District of Missouri asking if I was still interested in taking a position with their office. STILL INTERESTED? This had been my goal for years. I had applied for the position earlier that year and assumed I did not get the job. I hurriedly returned his call and told him yes, I was very interested and wanted the position. He indicated that once I passed the background investigation, I would be hired. I started with the office in downtown St. Louis in August 1999. I was still trying to get my bearings and acclimate myself to this new position, when in September 1999, my father called to tell me that my mother likely had an acute form of leukemia. Leukemia! On top of everything else she was suffering with, how could this be? He was very distraught, an emotion he rarely displayed. Our family prayed and cried and knew this must be the beginning of the end. How could she fight cancer as well?

ALLISON—September 9, 1999: Tomorrow we will know if the leukemia is treatable. Regardless, I guess the outcome isn't that good. Everyone is a mess. Life is a mess. Dad is beside himself with worry. He's been trying to be strong but I know he's been crying. I am like a zombie to balling. We are all so stressed out. I did get the Feds job and this is my second week. I love it but can't concentrate. Mom's getting a lot of visitors and a lot of prayers. When I went to see her on Wednesday she was so strong, saying it will be okay, God has a plan. She doesn't seem angry or scared or anything.

In the fall of 1999, with some sort of premonition that the end was near, my mother began crafting poems for everyone she knew. She had always loved to draft rhymes in her head for special occasions, birthdays, or anniversaries, but this was somehow different. These poems were distinct ways for her to honor and thank the special people in her life. The poems are all dated August or September 1999, addressed to her closest friends, relatives, sisters, her mother, and even the nurses at the hospital. Since her hands would no longer perform, my sisters or I would type or write what she recited, playing back the previous line so she could construct her words to form the rhythm she intended.

Less than a month later, the doctors informed us that leukemia had been a misdiagnosis, that possibly medication had caused a breakdown in Mom's bone marrow. We were elated! I remember going to visit my mother during that time, early October, and the air was crisp but the sun shining. She was at Barnes Hospital–West location, which had a small pond with ducks on the hospital grounds. I wheeled Mom outside, and we celebrated the good news. I recall gazing at her as she lifted her face to the sun, eyes closed, feeling the Indian Summer's warmth on her cheeks. She was released home soon thereafter.

On October 9, 1999, we all met at my parents' house for dinner. Mom stayed in her bedroom, as I mentioned, while we ate. She joined us in the family room after dinner, but she tired easily, so Dad put her back in bed. Before my husband and I left, I went to her room to find her curled up on her side. She was awake but looked small and frail and almost childlike. "Bye, Mom, I love you." She said goodbye and told me she loved me too.

ALLISON—October 9, 1999: Mom isn't doing too well. She's down a lot and just doesn't have much to enjoy in life. I know she doesn't want to live like this, she hates the tracheotomy. She just seems so uncomfortable and sad. It makes me so sad, wondering how she can find the will to live.

On October 12, 1999, I left the office early to do field work. In my job, we are required to conduct home visits on offenders under federal supervision. We check in on them, make sure they are abiding by the conditions of their supervision, living where they have reported, and so forth. My field partner and I did a few visits and then stopped for a bite to eat at

Crown Candy Kitchen, a St. Louis landmark, known for malts and shakes and sundaes that are out of this world. We hadn't known each other long, so our conversations were still of the "get to know you better" variety. We were discussing our families and I said something that upon reflection, seems very strange to me. I said to him, "My mother is dying, she has multiple sclerosis." I had never before that day described my mother as "dying." I'm not quite sure why I did then, other than perhaps for some dramatic effect. I was quite dramatic in my younger years. We finished our field day and I began driving home. I had to pass my parents' subdivision on the way to my house and I had finished work a bit earlier than usual. As I drew near to their home, I thought, "I should stop in and see Mom." But I didn't.

It was Wednesday, October 13, 1999. The telephone rang at roughly 3:30 a.m., and my husband answered. I think most people would admit they get a bad feeling when the phone rings in the middle of the night. It's never good news, is it? The memory is vivid. The ringing pulled me from a hazy dream. My husband said in to the receiver, "She did?" Then he handed me the phone. It was my father. "Allison, I think your mother passed away tonight." Even now, he is trying to protect me, I thought, soften the blow, by using the words, "I think." He, in fact, knew. Rob and I stepped out of the bed, and I fell into his arms, collapsed. My legs had buckled beneath me. We dressed in the dark, in silence, and then drove to my parents' house. My father sat in the kitchen in his pajamas; a police officer sat in another chair. I slowly walked to their bedroom to see her, stiff and cold. I returned to the kitchen and, eventually, the men from the mortuary wheeled her out. I could see them out the kitchen window. We sat and stared at one another, just stared.

After . . . within hours, I guess still in shock, we were throwing away all of my mother's medications and anything health related. Pill bottles, suction tubes, and bandages were all quickly delivered to a large, dark Hefty bag. Dad asked Rob to take the wheelchairs to the basement. The morning after, or really, the morning of, hours later, was spent making telephone calls to my grandmother, my mother's sisters, her friends. My father made most of the phone calls, but I made a few. Some people were very upset, and others, like my grandmother, simply responded, "She did?" My grandmother was a wonderful, loving woman, but admittedly, couldn't cry. She had now outlived two of her daughters. My Aunt Clodie, my mother's younger sister, quietly told us that she woke in the night, around 2:00 a.m., and a hymn was parading through her mind. The words to the hymn describe entering God's grace. It was likely the precise time my mother's soul was doing just that.

That afternoon we went to the funeral home to pick out a casket, a surreal experience. We brought the clothes she would wear, the dress she had worn at my wedding. The next day we met with our pastor to discuss the service, what he had prepared and what we wanted to add. He said an interesting thing to my sisters and father and me. He said, now that you have experienced it, you will be more compassionate and have a better understanding of someone who loses their mother, or wife. You will know how they feel, to an extent. A friend of mine lost her mother a few years later, and I felt like my friend was drawn to me at the wake. She knew that I knew.

The pastor also told us time would help, but in five years or ten years we may have a day when we are grieving just as we did that day, on day two, After.

In this dream, I am roughly eight years old. I am standing in the doorway to my mother's bathroom. She is sitting on a stool that has golden legs and a plush, pink-padded seat. She is teasing her hair. She is wearing a long green dress with golden embroidery around the neck. She and my father are going to a black-tie affair. She looks so beautiful. I don't know she is sick, she doesn't look sick. She is beautiful.

After . . . I had that snapshot from the beach enlarged after my mother died, and when I went to pick up the picture at the photo shop, a day before her funeral, the shop attendant looked at the photo, smiled and said, "She looks so happy, at peace." He had no idea . . .

The wake . . . we see her for the first time in days. We are alone with my mother in a dimly lit room flooded with flowers. To this day, I hate carnations, because their scent reminds me of death. Dad tells me to kiss her, but I don't want to. It isn't her, it's a dead body, and it freaks me out. But he is just standing there, waiting, so I kiss her on the cheek.

The funeral was held on a Saturday. I don't recall the weather. I don't recall what I wore or ate for breakfast. I have only hazy memories of the saddest day of my life. I suppose we imagine we will remember every small detail, and perhaps some do, but I don't. I remember the service, listening to "Ave Maria" and "How Great Thou Art," two of my mother's favorite songs. I remember the pastor describing my mother's life as a work of art, a painting. However, as with most watercolors, there are shadows of gray, as there were in her life. The shadow that is multiple sclerosis. I spoke at the funeral, my knees knocking as I stood at the front of our church. My aunts also spoke, reminiscing about the childhood they shared with my mother, their big sister. "She was the first to go to school, the first to take piano lessons, the first to drive, the first to date, the first to go to college, and the first to marry." And on October 13, she again "went first."

Before the lid of the casket is fastened, letters from Megan and Emily are slipped inside. And as one last gesture, my father presents the porcelain angel. The casket door is closed, the porcelain angel by her side.

ALLISON—October 26, 1999: I guess I've been putting off writing because I hate to write what I have to write. Mom died on 10-13-99.

ALLISON—November 2, 1999: I miss touching mom—scratching her arm. I saw her the Saturday before she died and now I wish I had held her longer or told her I loved her one more time. . . . Dad wanted to see mom by that Friday, I know he was really missing seeing her. We were all nervous for Friday night—the visitation. You're just scared how she will look or how you will react and act to people. It went better than we thought—Dad held up really well. It was nice to see all those people and flowers, there for mom. It makes you feel good to see certain people, that you can't believe would come. Saturday morning was hard, saying goodbye and seeing mom for the last time, but you realize the body is just a shell. The funeral was such a tribute to her and it was neat to hear different people's stories about mom. It was nice for me to be around the Bible Study ladies because those were mom's best friends and I just felt closer to her by being around them. The whole weekend I just felt so thankful to be part of such a loving, caring family. I don't know what I'd do without them. On October 12, Tuesday, June [my mother's good friend] visited mom for a few hours and mom told her she was tired of fighting—she was ready.

After . . . I am angry. Angry at God. I quit attending church, even though I know my mother would be so upset by it. She raised us to be spiritual and read the Bible and worship. But I have no desire to worship. I feel that God has taken her too soon, even though I suspect she is in a better place. My life's course is altered, all because I have lost her.

In this dream, I enter a crowded room and surprisingly, I see my mother on the other side. I can't believe she is here! She is standing, no wheelchair! I am trying to make my way across the room, to maneuver through the dots of people. The closer I get, the farther away she appears. People keep stopping me, interrupting my path. "Let me through, my mother is here!" But when I arrive on the other side, she isn't there.

After . . . I begin to question my own mortality. Am I happy with my life? I now feel like I can take chances and be reckless because I don't know how much time I have left. I want to play with fire. God won't take me until I have worked through my demons and fears about death. Rob and I slip farther from one another. We develop separate interests, separate friends, separate lives. We eventually become roommates, passing in the hall and kitchen.

After . . . it is December 1999. I am struggling with the first Christmas without Mom. She loved the holidays and decorating her home with Santas, garland, and trinkets galore was an all-day affair. She would have us girls play her holiday classics (LPs!) on the record player as she directed us around the house, defining which decoration went on which bookshelf or table or mantle. She had sewed stockings for each of us when we were young and her hands obeyed. These hung proudly above the crackling fire and were always filled with fun items, walnuts, and a tasty orange. So, as the cold air blusters in this December and she is gone, I have no desire to buy an evergreen, much less decorate my own home. I tell my father as much. The next evening, I arrived home from work and standing on my front porch was a Christmas tree. Attached to one of the fragrant branches was a note, penned by my father. "Your mother would be upset if you don't have a Christmas tree this year." He was right. So, I draped it with twinkling white lights, unwrapped my favorite homemade ornaments, and reminisced about all the Christmastimes that my mother made so special.

2000

(I am thirty-three)

After . . . my father hosts a "family meeting" to explain how my mother's trusts will be divided. Diana will receive her portion now; Carolyn and I will each receive a lesser sum and more on our thirty-fifth birthdays. Money can make life comfortable. Can I choose to have my mother back instead?

My father insists that each of us select our favorite music boxes from Mom's vast collection. Megan and Emily, Aunt Carol and Aunt Clodie will also receive a winding treasure. Twelve years later, my delicate box proudly sits on the bedroom windowsill. It is squarely shaped, showcasing peach and white flowers and moss-colored leaves, all made of silk. Two baby-blue butterflies, with gold-glittered dots accenting the wings, peak out from the flowers below. When I turn the crank beneath the box, it plays "Shadow of your Smile," as the butterflies rotate, as if in flight.

After . . . It is Mother's Day, 2000. I go to the grocery store and approach the seafood counter to buy some salmon. After he wraps the fish, the clerk smiles and proclaims, "Happy Mother's Day!" I say thank you and suppress my seething retort, "I am not a mother and I no longer have one!"

ALLISON—May 20, 2000: This morning I thought of the time Carolyn and Diana and I brought mom to the spa. It was only about 2 years ago. I went in the room with mom and she got a facial. I still remember how much she enjoyed it and how cute she looked with that mask on her face. I think she got a manicure too. It made me sad to think of it though, how much I miss her. I just wish I could talk to her again or touch her hand. I wish she would send me a sign, that she's okay— safe—better off. I guess anything could be a sign but how will I know for sure? Death is so strange, life is so strange.

Up until the year 2000, I had blindly convinced myself I did not enjoy running, certainly not long distances. I attribute this to a popular but nasty classmate, who commented in the seventh grade that I "run funny." It's amazing what one statement can do for the self-esteem and future convictions of a young woman. So, it seems ironic that the year after my mother's death, I took up this sport. Several men in my predominantly male office ran at lunchtime, and one day I decided to join them. Initially, I could barely run a mile, and as the guys kept their stride, I walked and tried to catch my breath. But as the days and weeks dragged on, eventually I could run two miles, then three. Twelve years later, I can say that running fuels my soul. I ran my first half marathon in 2005, my second in 2010, and my third in 2011. I prefer four to five miles, and feel so strong when I am on a good pace. I often think of my mother and the fact she would have given anything in those later years, to walk, much less run.

2001

(I am thirty-four)

After . . . I am having trouble remembering her voice.

ALLISON—September 12, 2001: There isn't a cloud in the sky . . . nor an airplane. Our world will never be the same. Yesterday, 9-11-01, the World Trade Center was leveled by terrorists. Terrorists hijacked 4 planes; 2 hit the WTC, one hit the Pentagon and one crashed in a field in Pennsylvania. It is just devastating. It's so awful, the people on the planes knew they were being hijacked and were likely going to crash. People were jumping out of the WTC to their deaths. Firefighters and police officers are missing. I was at work yesterday morning and Carolyn emailed me around 8:15am asking if I'd heard about the WTC, which I hadn't. I called Rob and he turned on the TV and gave me updates. Finally @ 11am we were allowed to leave the building. The building was sealed off by the U.S. Marshals, they had dogs and guns, etc. We were off today, thankfully. They said on the news that 50,000 people work in the WTC. This has really made me think about life. I don't want to take anything for granted, my family or friends. . . . The government suspects Bin Laden, an Afghan terrorist. This will change things forever. . . . Please help us God.

ALLISON—September 16, 2001: War is imminent. Today is such a gorgeous, peaceful day. Not a cloud in the sky and yet that fact remains . . . war is imminent. All Americans are wondering, when? When will we strike? It seems as though life will never be the same. It's been 5 days since the terrorist attack. The news is saturated with stories, so many personal accounts—so horribly sad. You just want to wake up and be told it was a horrible nightmare. I thank God I've been spared having to have been an eyewitness, or losing someone dear to me. Patriotism is amazing. There are American flags everywhere. But our military is preparing for war. They believe the attack was organized by Bin Laden and Muslim groups in Afghanistan. The actions he takes will determine President Bush's place in history. His actions will determine the future for this country. . . . No professional sports this week, the stock market has been closed since Tuesday, commercial flights are just getting back under way. It's a strange feeling now to see an airplane up in the sky because you know the passengers must be fearful. I will be. I've never been afraid to fly, but I will be now. There just seems to be a sense of hopelessness. Like, does anything really mean anything? But I feel differently towards people, more tolerant, more flexible, less angry, which is strange. I'm angry at the terrorists but now feel a bond with other Americans because you feel like everyone is suffering and scared. Life's little problems, dilemmas, disappointments seem so trivial in light of everything that happened.

It was around this time that Dad treated Carolyn and me to dinner at Remy's Kitchen and Wine Bar, a local restaurant with wonderful flair and delicious food. The walls are painted with colorful wine quotes and whimsical figures. A small votive flickered on our table, and as we were savoring our appetizer of stuffed grape leaves and hummus, Dad posed a question I absolutely never thought I would hear my father utter. "How would you girls feel if I were to go on a date?" I can't imagine the expression on my face. It was not that I didn't want my father to meet someone. He had been so incredibly lonely and his despair was almost tangible. Carolyn and I had secretly suffered with our own feelings of guilt when we could not spend time with him or for some reason left him alone on a holiday or special occasion. Even the thought of him dining alone each evening in the home he had shared with Mom was nearly unbearable. So, as my jaw dropped in amazement at his words, it wasn't that I didn't want him to gain some companionship. What I couldn't wrap my mind around was how in the world did my father meet a woman? Let there be no mistake, my father is very handsome, with piercing, sky-blue eyes, muscular calves, and a very quick wit. But he is quiet, sometimes stoic, and not the type to strike up conversation or be outwardly charming. After Carolyn and I recovered from our initial state of shock, we gave our stamp of approval to any future courting. I had several friends ask how I was going to manage. I suppose I knew that my father would never forget or replace my mother, nor would he embarrass us and date a woman younger than his daughters! Though I had always felt that my mother had been cheated out of so much of life, honestly, my father had too. The weeks and months and years he spent hospital bound could have been spent otherwise. But he would never have been anywhere else. Perhaps now, life could be easy for my father. Perhaps now he would meet someone who could take care of him for a change.

ALLISON—October 5, 2001: Carolyn passed the bar exam! It was so exciting and I'm so happy for her!! Last Friday, dad, Carolyn and I went to Jefferson City for her swearing in. It was really neat. I was so proud of her. I've been thinking about mom a lot. It is almost 2 years, 10/13. It's silly little things that cause the memories to flood my mind. Yesterday I was flipping thru the movies on TV and I saw that "Lucas" was on. I remember watching that with mom and she cried for the little boy in the movie. I miss her so much. What an original mom was. I am so lucky, that she was my mother, that I knew her.

My parents owned a huge contraption of a bed. I suppose it was a king size, but each side had a remote control so the sleeper could adjust it to their liking. The top portion of the mattress could be raised or lowered upon the push of a button. This was where we often watched television or movies with Mom. On that particular day I recalled from my past, I was lounging on Dad's side of the bed and Mom was on her side. We both had our mattresses raised, so we were sitting, as though in recliners, and watching *Lucas*. I remember glancing at Mom, and tears had formed in her beautiful blue eyes. Mom was always compassionate to the ill or infirm, or just the kid who got left out or teased. *Lucas* was obviously not a blockbuster or Academy Award–winning movie. This was not a day or event that should have been memorable or even special. But these moments are what form the kaleidoscope of a person, the small bits and pieces we remember as they entwine with one another to reveal the soul.

ALLISON—November 11, 2001: I miss mom so much. There are so many times I can close my eyes and imagine the last time I saw her alive. She was lying in her bed, on her side with her hands up by her chest. She looked so sweet. I hugged her goodbye and told her I loved her.

2002

(I am thirty-five)

In February 2002, my office sent me to San Francisco for a conference. This was my first "working vacation," and I intended to make the most of it! I have always loved traveling, eating, sightseeing; just being alone has never bothered me. I always have my journal in hand so if I am feeling a bit uncomfortable, I can write and no one seems concerned that a young woman is sitting alone. If I am in a restaurant, the waiter may question my identity. Am I a critic? Analyzing his every move? It can be a devilish cat-and-mouse game . . . is she writing about me?

ALLISON—February 5, 2002: I am in San Francisco!! I am sitting at Scala on Powell Street eating lunch. So far my trip has gone very smoothly. I left St. Louis at 8:40 this morning and got into San Fran at 10:45am. I took the shuttle to my hotel, the Andrews. I have to stay at another hotel for the conference. I can't believe my office let me come. . . . Okay, now I'm at dinner—at Plout. I'm enjoying Ahi Tuna, over lentils and spinach in a red wine sauce—delicious! It's noisy and my chair is uncomfortable but I don't care, I love it! I shopped this afternoon, walked to Chinatown. When I got back to the hotel I was feeling very lonely and sort of down. I considered staying in! Then I looked in the mirror and said, "Allison! This is an opportunity of a lifetime! Get out to this city!"

ALLISON—February 6, 2002: I just laid in bed and listened to the morning sounds of the city. The hotel has breakfast on each floor so I went out there and got a coffee, scone and an orange, yummy. I'm just really trying to appreciate the little things. Last nite at the restaurant, as I was writing in my journal, the French waiter asked, "are you going to put my name in your book?" He was funny. I'm not sure what to do today, I have the whole day free. . . . I'm at dinner—at Moose's. What a good day. After breakfast I ventured out. It was raining so I went to Café Espresso and got a delicious soy latte and sat and read my book until 10am when Sak's opened so I could buy an umbrella! I walked around downtown and searched for this sushi restaurant I wanted to try for lunch. The menu didn't impress me so I just headed back to the Andrews, checked out and got a taxi to the Holiday Inn, which is fine.

I then set out and walked to the Buena Vista, right around the corner and had an Irish coffee. I went to the North Beach and had lunch at this quaint little Italian restaurant, l'Osteria del Forno. I walked and walked and walked to the Pier and toured Alcatraz. It was very interesting. I did the audio tour and really enjoyed it.

ALLISON—February 9, 2002: Today is mom's birthday. In December I wrote a note to the ladies from mom's bible study and asked them if they would send me some memories about mom. They invited me to one of their meetings and I had such a wonderful time! Carolyn came also. They had so many funny, warm, heartfelt stories about mom and their time with her. I laughed and enjoyed myself so much—more than I do with most of my own friends. It led me to think about the relationships I have with my friends, none of which are that strong. Today, on the shuttle from the hotel to the airport, we stopped at the Hyatt. This woman and her friend were hugging goodbye. The woman called out, "bye, I love you buddy!" and got on the shuttle, teary-eyed. I wish I had a friend like that. I feel that way about Diana and Carolyn but I certainly don't have a friend I feel that close to. I guess I should be thankful that I'm so close to my sisters.

June, my mother's close friend and Bible study member, who had shared my mother's last afternoon with her, sent me these words after Carolyn and I attended their meeting in 2002: "As Jane and I talked that last afternoon [10-12-99], she wanted to share and have me read the letters her sisters had written to her and also a piece Ali had written. They were in her dresser, in a special box. We talked of how Jane had discovered and shared the strengths and talents that were uniquely her own. She put her best into each thing or hurdle that presented itself and seemed to square away the situations to be tolerated, of how she would seek to find what was positive in people and events. On that day, she carefully named Rex, each daughter, granddaughter, and son-in-law by your real name (not the nicknames), with her own voice, out loud. She spoke of how proud she was of each person and all they had become. She talked of her mom and family and their strong foundation. Jane was grateful to each of her family, whom she felt offered her the warmth, attention, and compassion that made her life worth living, not just existing. Jane found joy in living, thanks to her family and some way, somehow, found peace within herself.—June"

ALLISON—Spring 2002: Saturday night we went to dinner with dad and his new woman, Becki. I like her so much. She and dad are together almost every day! I'm so happy for him, he was so lonely and bored. I'm just excited he's getting to do all those things he and mom never got to do. And Becki seems to have no desire to replace mom or upstage her. She seems very confidant and outgoing. I hope things work out for them.

After . . . Several years following my mother's death, my sisters and I decided to participate in the fifty-mile MS Challenge Walk. Somehow I had been selected to be on the inaugural St. Louis Gateway Chapter Challenge Walk committee. At the first committee meeting, I listened to the details of the journey and began daydreaming about making the trek with my two sisters, in honor of our mother. Could the three of us really walk fifty miles? I knew the biggest challenge would be raising $1,500 each, as none of us are salespeople. But once we began training and sending letters to family and friends, the donations came pouring in. On one of our training walks, Carolyn was complaining about her new shoes, and after inspecting them further, we realized she was wearing golf shoes (and *she* graduated from law school). In the darkness of the morning, she had accidentally slipped her feet into the wrong pair.

The challenge walk finally arrived, and what a joyous experience for the three of us! I made us each a blue-beaded bracelet that read "Mom" to wear during the event. We met in the early morning hours on a Friday and set out for our three-day journey through Illinois and Missouri with 130 other walkers.

The walk took place in June 2002, as the temperature neared 90 degrees. We walked and talked and laughed and reminisced about Mom and days gone by. There were rest stops every three to four miles with granola bars, peanut butter, and Gatorade. We took pictures along our route and to pass the time, belted out show tunes, "DOE, a DEER, a female deer, RAY, a drop of golden sun!" Friday: nineteen miles. We slept on cots in a school gymnasium but not before receiving free massages from local massage therapy students! Saturday: twenty-one miles! That evening at the pit stop, the MS Society held a candlelight ceremony. All of the walkers gathered and each held a candle. When the chapter president read your reason for walking, you stepped into the circle. So, the first reason being, "I walk because I suffer from MS." Several walkers stepped into the circle. Some individuals who made the move forward shocked me, as I had no idea after walking miles beside them, that they had been diagnosed with this disease. The next reason, "I have lost a loved one to MS," and my sisters and I and several other walkers stepped into the circle. The reasons were read one by one, until everyone had joined the circle. It was a tearful experience, but I had never before felt that kind of genuine, communal compassion in my life. The committee had asked me to make a brief presentation about my mother and her struggle with MS, so I conveyed what I could through this poem:

[Allison] 6/1/02: <u>MS Challenge Walk</u>
When I was just a young girl,
Around the age of three,
My parents received that dreadful news,
and wondered how their future would be
My mother, a vibrant woman,
then the age of thirty-five,
Had grown up a poet, dancer, musician,
a mother of three and so full of life.
She had guessed even before her doctor,
That the numbness in her hands
Of how she suddenly had become clumsy
Meant for her, God had a different plan.
Of course, I was just a little girl then
One sister younger than I,
An older sister who knew our mom was "sick"
But as our childhood flew by . . .
She had cookies waiting when we arrived from school
Attended every swim meet and dance
Then came the cane, then came the wheelchair
But she never gave up on the chance . . .
That one day there might be a cure for her
That she one day might walk again
That though multiple sclerosis was waging a war
Somehow she would win.
So my parents' lives took a turn
They never suspected when saying "I do"
And my sisters and I, who are here tonight
Witnessed their struggle as they saw it through.
Our mother always had a smile
Despite the pain she often endured
She was a constant, loving reminder
That joy and laughter are a cure.

Our mother battled for twenty-eight years
A lesson that life's plans are never a lock
We are so grateful for all of you
Someone else will triumph since you have chosen to Walk.

Exhausted, my sisters and I collapsed into our dorm room beds at a local college and realized Diana had lost two toenails! Sunday was a mere ten miles. Ha. Our father met us at the finish line on Sunday with balloons and chocolates. We participated in the challenge walk in 2003 and 2004 and raised over $15,000 for the MS Society. The second and third years, the finish line was erected at Union Station in downtown St. Louis, and how exciting it was! As walkers finished, we were kept in a "holding area," with snacks and free beer donated by Anheuser Busch until all of the walkers had arrived. Then we walked together, arm in arm, to the finish line in the courtyard of Union Station. Union Station is a former train station that now holds shops and restaurants and an outdoor area, with ducks and paddle boats. Our father was there again, cheering us to the finish with roses and chocolates. The first year we participated we met two sisters whose father suffered from MS. It always felt strange to me to tell those walking for a loved one that our mother had died. I didn't want to scare anyone, especially those who had never let themselves consider the disease might be fatal. We fondly called those girls the "other sisters." They were back each year, walking together. In 2005, I saw the "other sisters" at an MS event and learned that one of them had been diagnosed with MS. Devastating. And something my sisters and I silently feared for ourselves.

2003

(I am thirty-six)

In February 2003, we planned another "Sisters' Weekend," this time for Phoenix, Arizona. We spent three days shopping in Scottsdale, sipping prickly pear margaritas, hiking near Tapatio Cliffs resort, and dining on southwestern fare. On most sisters' weekends, after a few sips of chardonnay, we engage in "topic talk." We take turns and select a topic to be pondered . . . the five destinations you must visit before you die . . . if you could build a home anywhere in the world, where would it be? . . . How would you spend one million dollars? At some point, our conversations become melancholy as we discuss our mother and how our lives will never be the same.

*ALLISON—July, 24, 2003: Carolyn, Diana and I went to dad's house today and cleaned the basement and the 3 of us walked around and picked out what furnishings we want. Dad and Becki bought a condo and are taking very few of dad's things. Carolyn, Diana and I went to dinner Saturday night (so fun!) and then watched all the old slides. It was so neat, but sad to see mom with us when we were little. Dad and Becki get married 9/6. It will be weird, I think. I'm so happy for dad but it's just strange. I wonder how he feels, he doesn't say much. He keeps saying "we both had 40 good years and now we're starting new lives.". . . **In the basement we found some of mom's diaries.** I feel a little weird about reading them but I feel so much closer to her when I do. . . . Grandma Rolston died today. She has been very sick the last few weeks so we were expecting it but it's still so sad. But I don't think she was very happy. She couldn't really see or hear and couldn't use her hands. Carolyn and I last saw her on Mother's Day—I'm so glad we went to see her. She was so happy to see us. I keep thinking about her in heaven seeing JoAnn and mom and grandpa. I wonder if it's really like that . . . joyous and exciting, seeing your loved ones???*

ALLISON—August 1, 2003: Grandma Rolston's funeral was on Monday. I got more emotional than I thought I would. I was sad last Thursday after dad called, but more so because I was flooded with memories of mom. The service was nice and then Aunt Clodie gave dad a box and bag of Grandma's papers to go thru as he is executor of her estate. It seemed so sad to me—93 years of life—in a box and a bag. Just makes me realize how unnecessary all of life's "stuff" is. It was nice seeing all of the relatives but strange also, like we'll all drift apart now . . . and we probably will. Diana, Carolyn and I went up with dad. It was fun spending time just the four of us. I think the whole event made dad emotional too, like a part of his life had ended with grandma's death. The cemetery scene was surreal. It was overcast and cool, almost like a movie, standing among the headstones.

ALLISON—September 8, 2003: Dad got married on Saturday, 9/6. A few years ago I couldn't have imagined I would ever be writing that sentence. I was sort of a wreck last week. I had so many mixed emotions. Mainly, I was feeling bad for mom, as she was so cheated in life. I doubt she felt that way, she was happy and often felt "lucky." It's scary when life changes . . . and I guess the wedding for me, signified a finality, dad has really moved on. I cried a lot last week. But, I was also really excited for the weekend!

My father and Becki were married in the same church where Rob and my nuptials occurred, so it was strange, knowing how much Rob and I had drifted apart over the years. Our relationship was now so different than when we said, "I do." This was also the same church where my mother's funeral took place. An uneasy excitement but restless nervousness brewed inside of me that week. It was exciting to see family and friends who had arrived in town for the big event. My mother's sisters attended, because they obviously loved my father for all he had done for their sister throughout the years and they had also grown fond of Becki. My sisters and nieces and I enjoyed pedicures, accompanied by champagne, and drafted a poem to read at the reception. The service was nice, and the pastor made mention of the fact that Dad and Becki had both had wonderful marriages but had also lived through sickness and the deaths of their partners. It was difficult to grasp that my father was now saying vows to another woman. My uncle's wife pulled me aside during the reception and said, "No matter how difficult, nothing will bring your mother back." She added, "everyone needs someone."

In October 2003, I started practicing Bikram Yoga. Carolyn encouraged me to try the workout one afternoon, and after my first session, I initially thought I might strangle my sister. Bikram is a series of twenty-six poses, performed in a 100-degree room for ninety minutes. Nine years later, I am committed to this practice and love it. Bikram yoga is like nothing I have ever experienced, and each class is a challenge. It is never easy but always worthwhile. It is another way for me to use, stretch, and exert my body in ways my mother never could.

ALLISON—October 23, 2003: Today was a weird day. I worked in the field alone, which I enjoy sometimes. I went to see one of my offenders at Barnes Hospital who had been in a motorcycle accident, and I was flooded with memories . . . the parking garage, going up the escalator . . . the skywalk and the patients' floors . . . the smells . . . the noises . . . just the emotions. I remember being anxious about how mom would be or feel or look. I have been thinking about mom <u>so much</u> recently. Carolyn and I went to the cemetery on Sunday. We read the Rose poem and we brought fall flowers. I can't believe it has been 4 years. In some ways, I feel like I'm just now returning to my old self. I've done an awful lot of soul searching these past 4 years. I find, lately, that the smallest, most unassuming thing can make me think of mom and become overwhelmed with emotion.

After . . . I continue to visit her grave, about twice a year, because it is in Illinois, a distance from my home. The drive is soothing, especially in the fall when the leaves look as if they have been dipped in paint buckets of gold, auburn, and red. The air is brisk and clean. Most of the journey is a winding two-lane highway through small, rural Illinois communities, with signs that read, "Welcome, population 400." Once there, I talk to my mother and tell her what has been happening in our lives. I place new flowers on the headstone, which also bears my father's name and date of birth. I tell her of all that has changed in our lives since she has been gone.

2004

(I am thirty-seven)

ALLISON—January 29, 2004: I miss mom so much. She pops into my mind at such odd times. Thoughts of her are triggered by such odd things. I heard this song, "100 years" while I was running . . . it's about having 100 years to live. I was getting chills and thinking about mom. I feel like she got cheated.

In March, Rob and I board a flight to Sarasota, one last ditch effort to save our marriage. The palm trees and blazing Florida sun welcome us as we again manage to entertain romance without intimacy. Flowers and champagne in the hotel room, gourmet seafood dinners at sunset, walks on the beach . . . yet we can't seem to connect. We behave as siblings or high school buddies, not as husband and wife. So, on our final night of vacation, we commit to a trial separation, though I suspect we both know there is nothing temporary about it. And though we had steadily progressed to this point, it came as a shocking and devastating blow to our parents and Rob's siblings. After hearing that my father shed tears at being ignorant to my unhappiness, it is the first time I am thankful that my mother is not here.

In April I rented an apartment in a hip area of St. Louis called the Central West End. My apartment was a loft with concrete floors, massive windows, and high ceilings. The transient neighborhood allowed me to venture out, walk to nearby restaurants and shops, and enjoy a newfound freedom. Rob and I maintained contact, because we shared "joint custody" of our dog, Sidney. Sidney spent two weeks with me and then two weeks with Rob. We feared he may develop some version of canine schizophrenia, but our sweet cocker spaniel seemed to easily adapt to this new lifestyle. Though I loved the independence I had gained, my life became a cycle of selfish indulgence. I had little, if any responsibility other than my job. I cooked for myself but became accustomed to dining out alone as well. I attended every new movie that arrived at the local theater, sought out culinary classes, and jogged at St. Louis' Forest Park. And though these weekends may sound like heaven to many, days could expire without me having spoken to anyone. I had lost my companion. I had lost simple conversation and often felt as though I might suffocate under the weight of loneliness.

ALLISON—June 26, 2004: Carolyn and Mark got engaged! Thursday night (6/24) in Maine! I guess he proposed in a lighthouse, then they went to dinner and to a pub, where his entire family was waiting. I can't wait to see the ring and hear more about it. They get home tonight. I stopped by there today and left a bag of 4 bridal magazines and card on their front porch—ha!

It was about time! Carolyn and Mark had been dating nearly ten years, and I doubted Mark would ever take the plunge. When we were younger and swam for our country club swim team, Mark had been one of our lifeguards. Of course, at that time, Carolyn was eight and Mark was eighteen, so sparks had not begun to fly. They became reacquainted after Carolyn graduated from college and began dating in 1995.

ALLISON—September 5, 2004: Carolyn has been busy, making wedding plans. I'm so excited for her and the wedding is going to be so wonderful, in Maine! We bought my bridesmaid dress last week and then she bought her dress! It is beautiful on her.

On a sunny November afternoon, Rob and I uncorked a bottle of cabernet sauvignon at "our" house and selected the items we each wanted to keep. We took turns, as though we were in school gym class, choosing the ideal "team" with which to move forward. It was friendly and systematic. We drifted through the hallways of our former life as photographs of those closest to us spied from the walls. A list was constructed, documented proof this was actually occurring. I left that evening, and as tears streamed down my face, I considered driving off the highway. My sports car would quickly slide down the embankment and perhaps this pain would end. Thankfully, Sidney sat attentively in the backseat and kept me from making such a stupid decision. Would I ever feel joy again?

Rob and I had come to realize that life is too short and neither of us was happy in our situation. Our thirteen years together officially ended later that month with two simple signatures, arguably one of the most uncomplicated, amicable splits in history. It saddens me, because he knew my mother and loved her, and no other man I am with will have that opportunity. Knowing the end result of our marriage, the fact we were never able to have children, was a blessing in disguise. Now that I am in the life I am in, I never feel regret. It was not in God's plan, and Rob now has a son of his own, with a new wife. I am happy he reached that pinnacle in his life.

2005

(I am thirty-eight)

ALLISON—January 23, 2005: Johnny Carson died today. It is so sad to me. I know that sounds strange but thoughts of him bring back so many memories for me, especially of mom and dad. I remember, [at our house] on Maymont, mom and dad watching Johnny. When I was too young to stay up, sometimes Carolyn and I would sneak behind the sofa and "spy." I'm sure they knew we were there! Then, being older, and watching Johnny with mom. He was 79—which scares me because dad will be 70 this year. I can't imagine if something happened to dad anytime soon. I would feel so lost.

Rose had been our next-door neighbor while Carolyn and I were growing up, and she had quickly become one of my mother's closest friends. As a benefit of that friendship, my sisters and I were often treated to Rose's delicious chocolate chip cookies. When Rose baked her famous cookies, they were gobbled up quickly and left you yearning for more. If she brought them over warm and gooey from her oven, life was even sweeter! My nieces soon learned the wonders of Rose's baking, and our family still talks about those cookies today. In the spring of 2005, Rose hosted a bridal shower for Carolyn. She invited Mom's friends from our former neighborhood, as well as the ladies from my mother's fifteen-year-long bible study group. It was a gathering of women who were all honored to have known Jane. The last gift Carolyn opened was a blue Tiffany box, with a note that read, "from your mother." My mother's friend, June, who had been with her the day before she died, explained the package. June told us that while Mom was alive, she often spoke of how she hoped Carolyn would marry Mark. One day Mom ordered the vase from Tiffany's catalog and after it arrived in the mail, she asked June for this favor. She told June she didn't want to keep the vase at her home, as she didn't want to risk Carolyn finding it and asking questions. So, Mom asked June to keep it safe and if Carolyn and Mark did marry one day, June could return the vase, and Mom would give it to Carolyn as a bridal shower gift. But Mom didn't make it to this day. June had forgotten all about the vase until she recently came across it during a spring cleaning venture. She remembered Mom's wishes. So, Mom did make it to this day.

On June 30, 2005, I deserted the 99 degree St. Louis heat and arrived in Portland, Maine, at dusk to a cool 60 degrees. The gang was all there! Everyone was so eager for the weekend ahead and to share in Carolyn and Mark's big day. On July 1, I woke to a cloudy, misty morning and met Diana, Megan, and Emily at a local hangout near the wharf, The Porthole, for breakfast. We shopped around Portland and then met Carolyn and Mark and the groomsmen that afternoon at the church for a wedding rehearsal. All five of us girls wept and feared what emotions lay ahead for the actual ceremony! Following the rehearsal, the bridal party and honored guests met at the Portland Harbor to board the *Windameer,* a wonderful sailing vessel! We set sail at 3:30 p.m. and skimmed the waters for two hours. Cocktails and coats, fog and conversation . . . are we the Kennedys? The boat docked on Peak's Island, Maine, and we debarked to a chilly, misty evening. The rehearsal dinner was staged at Jones' Landing, which hosted a nautical theme décor. Several of us snuck away to a nearby T-shirt shop to purchase Peak's Island sweatshirts to wear over our summer dresses! Carolyn and Mark had chosen table settings perfect for our feast . . . bright yellow lemon wedges wrapped in cheese cloth and tied with white ribbon held place cards, blue and white-checked napkins lay on the white tablecloths, and small votives lined the tables. The meal began with New England mussels, steamed with onion and garlic, followed by steamed lobsters, corn on the cob, tomato and mozzarella salad, and roasted new potatoes with rosemary. All the guests donned lobster bibs as the clarified butter dripped down our chins. We raised our glasses for toasts, snapped photos, and finished the festivities with strawberry shortcake and Maine Deer Tracks ice cream. An evening we will not soon forget! We all boarded the ferry back to Portland and snoozed with hopes the wedding day weather would not be a repeat of today.

On July 2, as I wrestled from my slumber, I anxiously pulled back the curtain in my hotel room, gazed into the sky and saw . . . SUN! I called Carolyn to wish her "Happy Wedding Day," and she replied, "Could it BE any sunnier?" I met Carolyn, the bride-to-be (B2B, as we had been referring to her for months), Diana, Megan, and Emily at the Paradiso Salon, where we all had our hair fashioned in to up-dos. Carolyn had small, delicate white flowers for each of us to wear in our locks. As we sat in our salon chairs, the bell on the front door jingled, announcing a visitor. Our father strode in with a long-stemmed red rose for the bride. Even the salon stylists wept at his gesture. After being beautified, we were driven to the church, where Diana and I hung wreaths twined with baby's breath. Diana (our very own Martha Stewart) had whipped up the wreaths at 1:00 a.m. that morning. After decorating the aisles with candles and tulle, we retired to the parlor to finish getting ready. We kept Carolyn in exile so Mark couldn't view his bride before she floated down the aisle.

ALLISON—July 2, 2005: We were ready—ten minutes to spare, just standing there, looking at each other! We headed towards the back of the church, it all seemed to go by so quickly. I don't think I even got to hug Carolyn but I did tell her she looked beautiful—like Grace Kelly. Carolyn looked so pretty, elegant—I looked at Mark to see his reaction when he saw her, but he just had a big grin. My knees were knocking! I had such butterflies! I held it together until the vows when Mark almost lost it. The ceremony was beautiful, went smoothly. Everyone gathered outside on the sidewalk, hugged and said hello. We took pictures outside the church then took the trolley to the ferry. Sunny, blue skies, 80 degrees! The ferry took us to Great Diamond Island, we walked down a gravel path where waiters were standing with vanilla vodka/pink lemonade drinks, garnished with strawberries and a fun 4th of July festive decoration sticking out. So cool and refreshing!

Walking to the tented area on Great Diamond Island mimicked a movie scene . . . a lovely pond decorated with a small wooden bridge and gazebo surrounded by Adirondack chairs lay to our right. On the left, the bay glistened in the sunlight and boats harbored at the pier, an absolutely idyllic setting. Tables were perched under the large tent, clothed in white linen, and adorned with yellow roses, coral zinnias, and white hydrangea flowers nestled in silver sand pails, and hurricane lanterns held blue, green, and white sea glass. The afternoon and evening progressed with cocktails, appetizers, dancing, and plenty of photographs. Children and adults alike played football in a nearby grassy area, while men smoked cigars near the pond. We all dazzled with celebrative sparklers for the 4th. Dad gave a heartfelt toast which began, "I know Carolyn asked her mother for a beautiful day and she delivered."

ALLISON—July 2, 2005: We all stayed until 8:45pm or so, walked to Great Diamond Island Inn and got a glass of wine there. I was carrying Carolyn's veil and had three people wish me congrats! Ha! Ferry ride—long, tired, dark, chilly. The band guys were hitting on Megan and Emily. Got to Portland and headed in to Ri Ra [an Irish pub]. Crowded and loud, but hey, we are in bridesmaids dresses!

The day after the wedding, I set out on an adventure of my own. I had decided to explore Maine. I was already there, had never seen that part of the country and was longing to broaden my view of the world. Though I was newly divorced and alone, I did not want that to stop me from traveling. On July 3, I rented a car, drove north to Freeport, Maine, and checked into the Harraseeket Inn on Main Street. I was given a wonderful room overlooking the garden, with a king-size bed, wood-burning fireplace, and quaint furnishings. Freeport's Main Street is lined with upscale outlet shops and cafes. I window shopped, then stopped at Azure Café, and was seated on the outdoor front patio, so I could watch families and couples enjoying their shopping experience. I relished a glass of Prosecco and steamed mussels. My journal entry describes a delicious dining experience, with an attentive and friendly waitress (very important when dining alone!) Upon returning to my hotel for the evening, I eased into the Broad Arrow Tavern and was seated at a great table on the patio, nestled next to a waterfall and beautiful perennial flowers. I ordered a Schrug Pinot Noir, a Maine lobster roll, and, of course, corn on the cob! I completed the experience with a warm chocolate chip cookie. Upon returning to my room, I built a fire, laid near the hearth, and watched old movies. I opened my window to allow the cool, east coast breeze surround me as I drifted away, maybe it was the wine . . .

> *In this dream, my mother is watching us, her daughters and granddaughters, dance. She is seated in the far corner under the tent, alone. She is wearing her mother-of-the-bride dress, but it looks like the one she wore to Diana's wedding, a pale dusty pink. So where are we? What year is it? My dress seems familiar. My mother is holding an orchid and she is smiling. I know she can't dance with us. Or can she?*

July 4, 2005—Independence Day! Freeport hosted an old-fashioned 4th of July parade on Main Street that I could view from my hotel. I felt as though I had been painted into a New England storybook. After watching the local high school bands, a waving mayor, and homemade floats, I checked out and drove south along winding dirt roads to the Harraseeket Lunch and Lobster Company. The restaurant was basically a shack on a pier, but a host of regulars lined the wood-planked sidewalk. Forty minutes later, I sat on a weathered picnic table bench and tasted the scrumptious crabmeat roll, french fries, and Whoopie pie I had ordered. Something I learned from my Maine vacation and continue to this day, is before traveling, I do my research. I pour over travel books and websites, seeking the most unique hotels and hidden treasures in dining. This was one of those times the guidebooks did not disappoint! I ventured from the lobster shack, eighty miles up Route 1 to Camden, Maine. Route 1 is a beautiful drive, with rolling hills. Lakes and piers play peekaboo through tall pines, and every so often a harbor housing sailboats comes into view. Once in Camden, I checked into the Lord Camden Inn and was given another wonderful room overlooking the main street and harbor.

ALLISON—July 4, 2005: I walked around Camden a bit, such a cute waterfront village. Walked to the Waterfront Harbor Café, another perfect table, outside, on the deck, overlooking the harbor. Sonoma Cutrer Chardonnay and delicious mussels— huge! 2 guys just asked 2 girls at the table behind me to go sailing and they said yes. They were obviously strangers. Crazy! The hippie woman at the table next to me said, "that's the reason they make 'America's Most Wanted.'" Ha, true!

ALLISON—July 5, 2005: Woke up and got breakfast in the hotel, took it to my balcony to eat. Went for a run thru Camden, such a cute town. I found some restaurants, possibly for dinner. Got ready and walked around–had delicious clam chowder and a blueberry ale (yum!) at Cappy's Chowder House. I sat at the bar and the bartender was great, very sweet girl—asked me about St. Louis. . . . I walked down to the pier and paid for my sailing cruise. The boat, the Appledone, was beautiful and huge! The owner, (looked like the Gordons Fisherman, but skinny— white beard) was totally hitting on me. He said I can use his cottage next time I'm in Key West—ha! He was a total egomaniac and I feared this would continue on the boat, but luckily, he didn't sail. The crew was nice and I talked to a few people on the sail. It was very relaxing, sunny but chilly! They served a great Bloody Mary. The sail was 2 hours.

ALLISON—July 6, 2005: Woke and walked to Cappy's Bakery, bought a blueberry scone and cappuccino, then walked to the park overlooking the pier, sat on a park bench and relaxed. It is sort of foggy, cool, slight mist over the water. I went running again—got ready and checked out. It took me over 2 hours to drive to Bar Harbor, lots of traffic thru Ellsworth—but overall the drive was beautiful. I stopped at a roadside stand near Bucksport and bought a pint of strawberries—delish! Arrived in Bar Harbor and got a lobster roll and chocolate chip cookie at the Lobster Claw. Tons of lobster meat. Very chilly outside, misty— so Maine! I checked into the Bar Harbor Inn and have a great oceanfront room with a balcony overlooking the water and rocks. I'm lonely tho—being alone is interesting. I read in my room, unpacked and just relaxed for a few hours. Walked around town and decided to eat at Café This Way—got seated but a waitress never appeared so I left. I was in such a quandary! Where to eat, what to do? I stumbled upon a wine bar—Aperitivo— had a Syrah and a delish cheese plate (tellagio, soft, brie-like cheese, buy this! Yum!) The bartender suggested McKay's for dinner so I headed there.

When the guidebooks fail you, ask the locals! I have made this a practice. Ask the bartenders, waitresses, and local shopkeepers where they would eat. I once met a girl in an airport; I was heading to "her" city, and she was journeying home. We sat in the airport lounge, and as she recited restaurants and fun hangouts, I scribbled onto a piece of scratch paper from my handbag. I would love to do the same for a visitor to St. Louis.

McKay's—very cool, old house, interesting art out front—I sat at the bar and had conversation with a few people. I had a Syrah/Merlot blend and the flat iron steak, mashed potatoes and green beans, all yummy. Then I got a glass of Prosecco with a blueberry buckle dessert—delish! 5 older gentlemen came in and sat at the bar and they were loud and talkative (from Texas). When I went to pay they grabbed my bill and paid it! (They have no idea how much I'd eaten!) Got back to my hotel, zzzzzzzz . . .

ALLISON—July 7, 2005: I went downstairs for the free breakfast and sat outside, watched the water and rocks—enjoyed the view. Then I walked the shore path, took pictures—must be 65-70 degrees – –cloudy but nice. I walked to Main Street and had lunch at the bar at Geddy's, which I feared would be "bar food" but was actually, great. I got the crab roll sandwich; fresh crabmeat, some mayo, avocado and swiss cheese on a fresh roll. I ended my meal with a blueberry wheat ale—he actually threw some blueberries in it! I walked down to West Street and got my ticket for whale watching. I was a little apprehensive, looked really "touristy" and I almost changed my mind—glad I didn't! Tho I was <u>freezing</u>, couldn't feel my fingers and every once in awhile I got a spray of water—I saw lots of finback whales, spouts and even 2 humpback sightings! I also saw harbor seals, gray seals and porpoise. It was awesome! Got back to my room @ 5:45pm and relaxed, balcony door open, listening to the surf. I finally decided to venture out a little after 7pm and walked to Havana. Wonderful! Several locals recommended it—so great! I sat at the bar and watched the bartender make several dozen mojitos! I had a Spanish wine, a Rioja, a delish salad of greens, raspberries, spiced pecans and guava vinaigrette. I then had the seared Ahi Tuna with mango. Of *course, I had to have a mojito—so that was my dessert! Walked back to my room, read and listened to the sea . . .*

ALLISON—July 8, 2005: Time to move on, almost home—I'm ready to be home. Drove 3 hours to Wiscasset and grabbed lunch at Red's Eats—famous spot (shack) by the water—got a crab cake sandwich and fries—ate while driving! Tricky—stood in line for almost 20 minutes to order. Food was great. But lonely . . .

My vacation ended the following day, but it is an adventure I will never forget. I knew from this day forward, fear or insecurity would not stop me from diving in to life.

2006

(I am thirty-nine)

Following my divorce, I dated a few men, but in 2006 I began a relationship with Steve. Steve and I were coworkers and had never considered each other more than fellow employees, until we attended a seminar together in Nashville, Tennessee. Nights of laughing, cocktails, and long talks led us to see one another in a new light. I am not sure if Steve and I were just more compatible or if I had matured, making this relationship so uncomplicated, loving, and pleasant. In the early days of our courting, I was struck by how differently different men respond to situations. I was surprised by Steve's reaction to events as it was often, so acutely, opposite of what I was used to with Rob. Steve soon became the love of my life and continues to be. He has heard stories and seen photographs, but the thought that he never got to meet my mother tugs at my heart on occasion.

When my mother was alive, she began to collect watercolor paintings by a local artist. All of the woman's artwork showcased butterflies. Most of the paintings were composed of muted shades of gray, blue, lavender, and green. My mother happened upon the artist at a St. Louis art fair and fell in love with her work. Each time they saw one another, the woman would remember my mother (likely because of the wheelchair) and they would share stories. I also purchased one of the artist's paintings, and for me, the butterfly came to signify my mother. In 2005 and 2006, I felt that I was also experiencing a "new life" or rebirth. So, just prior to my thirty-ninth birthday, I got my first tattoo! A butterfly. Though I chose the butterfly because of my mother, I knew she would not agree with my decision to go under the needle!

ALLISON—April 13, 2006: Today at the Cardinals game Carolyn told me she is pregnant!!!! We were going to get a beer and I said, "I'm getting a Newcastle, what are you getting?" and she said, "an O'Douls!" [nonalcoholic beer, so I knew] We hugged and talked about it for awhile. She's only about 5 weeks but goes for an ultrasound on Tuesday. Then she'll tell Diana when Diana gets here for our trip to Florida—next week! Yay!

The following week, Carolyn, Diana, and I enjoyed another "Sisters' Weekend" this time in Sarasota, Florida, our mother's favorite vacation spot. When she was alive, our mother often daydreamed about walking and driving again one day. She would describe to us how when this miracle occurred, she would buy a yellow convertible and wear a scarf around her neck. We could envision the scarf billowing in the wind, flowing behind her as she raced along the streets. So, as my sisters and I arrived in Sarasota, we rented a convertible for our weekend. We took the top down, tied matching polka dot scarves around our necks, and zoomed to our destination! Once at the beach, the three of us drew these words in the sand, "we're having a baby," and took photographs of our artwork. The picture had to be snapped quickly as the tide kept threatening our sand drawings. When we returned home, Carolyn showed the photograph to everyone, as a way of revealing her and Mark's "secret." Everyone was overjoyed. Megan and Emily had been waiting more than twenty years for a cousin on this side of their family, and Dad was finally going to have another grandchild. I suspect Carolyn longed to share her wonderful news with our mother.

ALLISON—May 20, 2006: Sunday was Mother's Day—difficult . . . I cried, thinking of mom.

ALLISON—November 15, 2006: Carolyn is going to have her baby in about 5 weeks! She's due 12/14/06. We went to lunch yesterday and I sense that she is getting more nervous. I pray everything goes okay. I can't wait to find out if it's a boy or girl!

Carolyn and Mark had a healthy beautiful baby girl on December 19, 2006, Eleanor Maeve. By the time Carolyn arrived in delivery, we were convinced she was having a boy. All of the old wives tales about the way a woman carries the pregnancy, the extent of her morning sickness, and her types of food cravings led us to believe the "femaleness" of our family was about to change. Carolyn and Mark allowed me to hover in Carolyn's room up until the final pushes, and for most of the day and evening, we called the unborn baby by the boy's name they had chosen. No wonder Ellie delayed her arrival for twenty-two hours.

2007

(I am forty)

ALLISON—December 12, 2007: One week ago, almost . . . on 12/6/07 we had to put Sidney to sleep. I'm so sad and have so much grief about it. I miss him so much more than I thought I would. I have cried every day since, I'll write more later, too sad now. But I can't ever forget how he looked at the vet's office, asleep on the blanket, so peaceful and cute. My heart aches.

Sidney's health had slowly deteriorated, and Rob and I were faced with the painful decision. We were still sharing joint custody, three years later. I remember speaking with our veterinarian, and he asked if Sidney was eating well—no; if he was excited when I arrived home from work—no; if he seemed playful—no. The vet explained that if I was answering "no" to each question, then Sidney was not enjoying his life any longer. Our dog's inability to stand on occasion or even walk outside to relieve himself finally forced us to end his long life. Rob and I met at the veterinarian's office on a cold, rainy December night and petted Sidney as he drifted off to sleep. Though Rob and I had divorced three years prior, the end of Sidney's life is what really brought that chapter to a close.

2008

(I am forty-one)

ALLISON—January 10, 2008: Dido: "If my life is for rent, and I don't learn to buy—well I deserve nothing more than I get, 'cuz nothing I have is truly mine." I've been so nervous about the move, selling my house, change . . . then I heard this song and really started thinking.

After much discussion, Steve and I decided to carry our relationship into a new phase and buy a condominium together. In January 2008, I put my house on the market, and it sold in ten days. I loved the home I had purchased in 2005, but Steve and I were ready to commit to a new life together. So, we thought it best to buy a place, one we could call "ours." We moved on a bitterly cold, but sunny day in February and were instantly compatible as roommates and lovers.

In April 2008, I began a journal for Ellie. A friend of mine has been sending a "birthday letter" to her daughter each year, highlighting the twelve months that have passed. She mails the letter so it is postmarked, but the envelope is never opened. When her daughter marries, she plans to give her the unopened letters she has been sending since her birth. I am now forty-one and realize I will not have a child of my own, so I decide to leave a sort of legacy for my niece. In the journal I note what is occurring in her young life, when she says her first words, what she likes to eat, the funny things she does. I also jot down the state of our world, major news events, and current political issues. I have not told anyone of the diary and look forward to Ellie's eighteenth birthday, when I can present her with the journal of her youth.

Megan, my dear niece, of whom my mother and I had both recorded her birth in our journals all those years before, became engaged in December 2007. She had dated Gary off and on for a number of years. The year of 2008 was spent planning, preparing, and sending emails to one another about the excitement of the wedding in August. She would highlight her favorite colors, pink and green. The nuptials would take place in Tulsa, and they would honeymoon in Mexico.

ALLISON—August 18, 2008: Diana called me today, broke into tears. She said Gary told Megan he is having second thoughts. The wedding is less than 2 weeks away! They are devastated. Even if he decides to go thru with it, they will have doubts. He can't explain it to Megan, just says he's not sure, doesn't want to lose his freedom. Diana was so upset. I felt sick to my stomach when she told me and I can't shake it. All the plans, excitement—ruined, regardless. How can Megan feel on top of the world knowing he has doubts. I wish I could help, I wish I had some words of wisdom. It's so awful, like Diana said, all those gifts sitting in her room. They have to pay for the caterer Friday.

The wedding was "back on," but Gary continued to express feelings of doubt the following week. Megan and Gary were both living in Dallas, and so, seven days before the wedding, Megan packed her car and bravely drove to her parents' home in Tulsa. She left her new home, her friends, her job, her life. The wedding was canceled. My sister had to call the guests, cancel all the arrangements, return the gifts and nurture a broken child. On the day that should have been the best of Megan's life, we all gathered at a house on the Lake of the Ozarks in Missouri. As we arrived, Megan stood in the driveway, a shell of herself. We hugged long and hard and I didn't want to let go. We went boating and waterskiing, barbecued, and played cards. We tried to distract Megan as the 5:00 hour approached, the time she should have been floating down the aisle. Ellie served as a wonderful diversion; an innocent child who had no idea of the devastation that was occurring in Megan's young life. But, as my mother gazed down from heaven on her first granddaughter, she likely knew that a better destiny lay ahead. Time would prove that Megan's decision to drive away from Dallas was the smartest resolution she had made thus far in life.

As we gathered at the lake in August, Megan told us she desperately needed a distraction. She began planning a "Sisters' Weekend" for all five of us, to New York City. Diana, Megan, and Emily flew from Tulsa, and Carolyn and I from St. Louis, on a Thursday in December. We met at the Warwick Hotel, amid a torrential downpour. The weekend was spent laughing, shopping, eating, and sipping wine. We joined the morning crowds outside the *Today Show* and snapped photos of Mathew Broderick, the guest for the day. We ice skated at Rockefeller Center and eavesdropped on a young couple getting engaged at the edge of the rink. We strolled through Soho and Greenwich Village and drew stares as we skipped down Fifth Avenue singing Christmas carols. Carolyn and I had a brush with fame as we entered our hotel elevator and rode eight flights with the actor, Ed Harris, and some of his friends. Too bad Megan, Emily, and

Diana chose to take a less-crowded elevator! (We continue to joke about this today.) One evening, while getting dolled up for a night in Times Square, we had plugged in several curling irons, hair dryers, and a small artificial Christmas tree. (I'm still not sure how Emily managed to pack that tree in her suitcase.) Diana plugged in an iron, and that was it, total darkness. We had blown a fuse and feared that maintenance would arrive for repairs and realize we had five guests in the room instead of two. We sent Megan and Emily to the lobby until a new fuse was installed, which as we discovered, didn't even require the maintenance man to enter our room. We joined the theater crowd to see *White Christmas* and sipped champagne at the Oak Bar in the Plaza Hotel. It was a fabulous trip. Megan's distraction mission had been accomplished. Her newly found love didn't hurt either.

2009

(I am forty-two)

ALLISON—January 18, 2009: Tomorrow is Barack Obama's inauguration— it is exciting. I hope things will turn around for our country. The economy is so bad, so many without jobs and money. We are very lucky. Emily got engaged! She pretty much knew it was coming since they had looked at rings. They are planning an October wedding. I think Megan is okay with it all, since she has Brandon.

ALLISON—February 9, 2009: Today would have been mom's 74th birthday— hard to believe it has been 10 years since she died. I drove up to the cemetery this morning. It is a beautiful day—70 degrees! In February! So, it was a wonderful drive. I listened to music and got upset on "Bridge over Troubled Waters." It always makes me sad, and makes me think of mom—especially the lines, "when you're weak" and "when pain is all around." I also listened to mom's funeral service, which I have on tape. I didn't get too down, I just miss her but I want to celebrate her life today! I brought some pretty spring flowers; pink, yellow, and purple, for the grave. Memories . . . I loved to walk into her bedroom and see her sitting up and smiling. If I saw her like that, I knew she was doing well. I wish I could hear her voice, it's hard to recall. My life is so good. I'm so lucky. I'm also so at peace now.

ALLISON—April 9, 2009: Megan got engaged! to Brandon on 4/1. She seems really happy—I haven't met Brandon, probably will next weekend. They want to get married next March in Sarasota! Fun! (I wish I could be in the room when Gary finds out! Haha)

ALLISON—May 22, 2009: Carolyn is pregnant!!! She went to the doctor today and he said all looks good—a faint heartbeat. Ellie is going to be <u>so</u> curious once she knows and especially after Carolyn starts showing.

Mom, I'm pregnant again! Mom, my daughter is getting married! These are the moments when we miss her most, those joyous occasions that occur in a woman's life that she longs to share with her mother. For years to come, my sisters and I will experience events, triumphs, and sorrows that only our mother can relate to and understand. I am torn with feelings of bitterness, sadness and yet, joy, when I look to heaven and somehow know that she knows.

ALLISON—September 2009: Wow! A lot has happened! Emily and Blake's wedding was beautiful! It was one of the hottest weekends of the year! But everything went so smoothly. Emily looked like the picture perfect bride! So beautiful. Diana was amazing, so organized, relaxed and had two brunches at her house! Megan was so supportive and sweet. Her wedding is on! 3/16/10 in Sarasota!

On September 19, I set out on another adventure. I had been chosen to become a firearms instructor for my district in addition to my other duties. I have no doubt this was because of my gender, not my shooting abilities. Regardless, I was pleased, excited, and nervous about the new endeavor. However, the position requires a two-week training period at the Federal Law Enforcement Training Center in South Carolina. I had attended training at the center before and knew what was in store . . . dorm rooms on a former military base, cafeteria food, and required uniforms. But, I love Charleston, so I could withstand the conditions. I decided to drive my new Jeep from St. Louis to the East Coast.

ALLISON—September 19, 2009: I left home at 9am in my new JEEP! Fun to drive! The ride seemed so easy, pretty uneventful but nice! Drove thru Illinois, Kentucky and Tennessee. Tennessee really is beautiful, lots of hills and trees and valleys. I listened to a book on CD so the time flew by. Arrived in Knoxville @ 5:30 pm, changed clothes and drove to Chesapeake's for dinner, a seafood place near the hotel. I had seafood gumbo which was delish! Perfect spice, shrimp and 2 huge scallops! Now I am having blackened Ahi Tuna with blue cheese butter and blue cheese grits! Peter Lehman Cab. Tomorrow I head to Charleston, bartender here told me to go to Justines, for soul food.

ALLISON—September 20, 2009: Woke at 6:30am, stopped at Starbucks. Hit the road and drove 6 hours to Charleston, Rain 7:30-10:30 UGH! Smokey Mountains were beautiful (drove thru North Carolina and South Carolina) but hard to enjoy with all the rain and white knuckling of the steering wheel! It was stressful!

The first day of class I met the other twenty-three participants in the program, probation officers from across the country, each representing a different district. The program is designed in such a way, that only those who have fairly good shooting skills should attend. After qualifying with a passing score on day one (90 percent or better), the remaining sessions are focused on improving firearm skills and knowledge as well as developing teaching points. After all, the goal of the program is to send twenty-four certified officers back to their districts so they can teach and train other officers. If you cannot pass the qualification course on day one, you are given a second chance on day three. If you fail to pass on day three, you are sent home without certification. None of the instructors in my district had ever been sent home for not passing. I was a bundle of nerves. On day one, I walked to the line among my classmates and could feel my heart practically beating through my chest. It felt as though you could see my shirt moving with each palpitation. We completed shots at the 1 ½-, 5-, 7-, 15- and 25-yard lines. The instructors then moved down range to calculate our scores. A hush fell over us as we all anxiously awaited our numbers. 88 percent. I was devastated, embarrassed, and trying desperately to control the tears from flowing. Most of the other officers were men, and I didn't want to show weakness or vulnerability. The pressure became immense. What if I didn't pass on day three? How would I face my colleagues if I were forced to return home early? Steve was extremely supportive when I called him in tears that evening.

On day three, our class was transported to an outdoor range near the base to practice drills and additional target shooting. It was mid-morning, and I knew my second qualification attempt would occur that afternoon. As I stood on the line, preparing to shoot on the instructors call, I noticed two beautiful butterflies flitting around near my paper target. I smiled. Mom was here. That afternoon I shot a 94 percent and fell to my knees in relief after my score was read. When I left the range that afternoon and glided out the door, I looked into the sky and a rainbow hovered overhead. I wasn't even aware it had rained.

ALLISON—October 19, 2009: Last Monday 10/12, Steve and I drove up to the cemetery and put fall flowers on mom's grave. Steve had never been and I think he enjoyed the drive. It was a bit overcast and the trees had not yet turned, but it was so nice. 10 years—it's hard to believe. In some ways I can't believe it has been 10 years and then when I think of how different my life is, it does seem like a long time. I miss mom so much. I wish she could know Ellie, and Steve. On 10/13 Diana called me and she was really upset, crying. I felt so bad for her, but I was at work and had to hold it together. Diana doesn't usually get upset like that. . . . I have been feeling so nostalgic lately—seems like I always do in October—not sure if it is the fall or because of losing mom in October and all that occurred afterwards. I woke this am, reminiscing about my house with Rob, remembering my life there. I don't miss that life but sometimes wonder about it. I think I would be miserable if I had stayed in West County, had kids and tried to conform. It's strange to think how unhappy and sad I was back then—it's hard to identify with those feelings, since I never have them anymore. I am so at peace and happy. I love my life and my life with Steve. We are so compatible and joke and laugh with one another. I don't take myself too serious when I'm with Steve.

ALLISON—November 7, 2009: I want to write a novel. I have kind of started it, I want to write about mom and M.S. and watching her struggle/battle and describing what it was like, from my perspective (the only one I know). I was thinking of using my journals (to remember) and also using the journals I have of mom's, from when we were little. We'll see, it could be really boring. I need to be able to describe "regular" life in an interesting way that readers would enjoy.

2010

(I am forty-three)

ALLISON—January 18, 2010: Baby is here! On 1/14/10 Finn Darragh was born!! He weighed 8 lbs. 5 oz. and came into the world at 1:48am. On 1/13 I was in the field [probation work], got home a little early and got in the shower. When I got out I thought I heard my phone ringing & when I checked I had about 6 missed calls from Carolyn and Mark! Carolyn was supposed to be induced on 1/14 but her water broke while she and Ellie were doing art at Yucando. Mark picked them up and drove to St. Lukes and I met them there. Carolyn got set up in her room and Ellie seemed so interested in all that was going on. Ellie and I left and I took her to the Bread Company and we had dinner. It was so fun, just her and I. She asks so many questions and is so curious. We went back to the house and watched "101 Dalmations" and I put her to bed and finally fell asleep myself @ 10:45pm. I woke @ 1:45am after having a dream that Carolyn had a boy with a really strange name. I couldn't fall back asleep and then Mark called about 2:30am and said they had a boy!

I wish I could hear and see my mother's response to learning we now have a MALE in our family tree. I have two sisters, three nieces, and, of my eight cousins, seven are females. I won't ever forget the hours after receiving the news of my first nephew's arrival. Ellie woke before sunrise and crawled into bed with me, dozing and innocent, she asked, "My mommy still at the doctor?" My stomach fluttered as I explained that her daddy had called in the night to tell us she has a baby brother. "I can play with him? And hold him?" she questioned. Upon my affirmative nod, she giggled and beamed, "I'm a big sister!"

Can life be any sweeter?

ALLISON—January 18, 2010: I'm so glad I got to be part of that experience with Ellie. She will not likely remember it—but I always will.

The next morning, Ellie and I pulled on our winter coats and rushed out the door, anxious to make Finn's acquaintance. We stopped and bought blueberry scones and bright daisies for Carolyn. Transporting a three-year-old kept my foot from grinding the accelerator, but I was so eager to get there and observe Ellie's reaction. I peered into the rearview mirror and saw her wiggling in the car seat. "Ali, I'm so excited!" she squealed. We arrived at the hospital and found Carolyn holding her bundle of joy. Ellie's diminished height prevented her from seeing Finn lying in the bed, so I lifted her up and placed her near Carolyn's side. She instantly wanted to touch, touch, touch, kiss, touch, kiss, kiss. A nurse wandered into the room and asked Ellie, "What do you think?" Ellie's instant response, "I love him."

In March 2010, my mother's first grandson made his debut in her favorite destination, Sarasota. Our family gathered among the Florida palm trees for Megan and Brandon's wedding week. Carolyn, Mark, Ellie, and Finn drove seventeen hours from St. Louis to Sarasota in a Honda SUV packed to its limits with the endless number of items required for a baby and toddler. We all met on St. Armand's Circle for pizza at Venezia and dined al fresco. Diana was able to score a sweet deal for all of the guests to stay at the Ritz Carlton at a discounted rate, which meant we had access to their swanky beach club. The beach club had been constructed on Lido Beach, just a few steps in the sand from where our family had spent our spring break vacations.

The rehearsal dinner played out at a festive Spanish restaurant on the Circle called the Columbia. I had dined many nights at the Columbia as a teenager, with my parents. As I laughed with the other guests, I turned to gaze into the dining room of the Columbia. The Spanish tiled floors and maple-colored wicker chairs sent my head spinning into another space in time. I fell through the rabbit hole and as if watching a film, I could see Carolyn and me, Mom and Dad, circa 1982, cracking stone crab and enjoying the delicious Columbia house salad. I was slumped over a bit, complaining of sunburn. (I refused to wear sunscreen as a teenager and always regretted it by nightfall.) Mom, Carolyn, and I had turned blonder with the Florida sun. Dad, with his rich, dark tan, relaxed in his chair, wearing white pants and a brightly colored tropical shirt. It was our family as it had once been. Suddenly, someone raised a glass of sangria and proposed a toast, "To Megan and Brandon!" I slipped back to 2010 and smiled. Life is still good; Mom is still with us.

ALLISON—May 9, 2010: Mother's Day—I'm feeling kind of down, sentimental, I guess, about today . . . not having mom. Mom would be 75 this year. I miss her and wish I could share things, life, with her. Emily sent me the sweetest text message today saying I'm a great aunt and friend. It really made me feel good.

In May, Dad celebrated his milestone birthday. Our entire family gathered at Steve's and my condo to honor Dad's 75th. We enjoyed a dinner buffet of barbeque, slaw, corn on the cob, and three pies baked by Diana. Though Diana is the oldest daughter, she is, surprisingly, also the most computer savvy. Using countless photographs dating back to 1935, she compiled a DVD, put to music, for our father. After dinner, we all joined together to watch Dad's life on the big screen. And though Dad mentions our mother less these days, watching the video there was no escaping the wonderful life they shared.

By the summer of 2010, I had been employed by the U.S. Probation Office for nearly eleven years. I began my career as a supervision officer, supervising offenders under federal Court jurisdiction. After several years of frustration with the criminal population and recidivism, I transferred to the presentence investigation unit, a role similar to the one I held with the state of Missouri. No longer was I charged with supervising offenders trying to reintegrate into society after being released from prison. I was now immersed in the "front end" of the justice system. I attended the plea hearing, interviewed the defendant, conducted a thorough background investigation, and then submitted my report to the sentencing judge. Presentence investigation reports for district court judges require an in-depth examination of a defendant's life, and as an officer of the court, I was also responsible for calculating the U.S. sentencing guidelines for each case. Sex offenses had become my specialty, and these were primarily the cases to which I was assigned. The Internet, though an amazing technological advance in our society, has also introduced an expanding market for child pornography. Men (and a handful of women) who used to sit in local parks ogling young boys and girls or relying on black market snail mail to receive pictures of minors in provocative poses can now access a limitless number of photos and videos of child pornography with a few clicks of a mouse. They steady themselves in front of the dim glare of their computer screen, in the privacy of their own home, and believe no one is watching. Luckily, detectives are watching, conducting undercover operations, searching for individuals downloading the obscene. The defendants charged in federal court are not viewing glossies of teenage girls in bras and panties. They are accessing the most sordid array of pictures portraying the molestation and rape of very young children, some bound with ropes or duct tape. Once you have seen the evidence, the images never escape your mind.

On one particular day that summer, I reported to court for my weekly sexual offender plea. As I entered the majestic courtroom, an average, fifty-something male stood at the podium shadowed by his attorney. The assistant U.S. attorney skimmed his file, awaiting the judge's entrance. The court reporter and clerk were positioned at the front of the courtroom, protected by mahogany and marble. The defendant's wife sat in the galley, in a wheelchair. The rustling of my papers echoed as the only noise in the courtroom. The judge gallantly entered, and we all stood in respect, except, of course, for the defendant's wife. The hearing progressed and ended with the defendant's pleas of guilty to receipt and possession of child pornography. Possession of child pornography carries no mandatory minimum sentence. Though a serious crime, those who possess the images have likely never had contact with the children depicted; they are only viewing the heinous work of others. Receipt, distribution, or production require prison terms, so I knew this defendant was now facing a minimum of five years in custody. The judge allowed him to remain on bond until sentencing, which was scheduled for October, due to his wife's "medical condition."

We left the courtroom in silence. The now-convicted offender and his attorney followed me to my office, where we commenced the interview. The offender informed me that his wife suffered from multiple sclerosis. He was not sure if I was familiar with the disease, but he explained the deterioration of her health as well as the crumbling of their marriage. I later wondered about their two teenage children. Did they fear life without their father as I once had? Or did they loathe him for what he had done to their mother and family? That October he was sentenced to sixty-three months in prison and following the pronouncement of sentence, the U.S. marshals placed him in handcuffs. As a businessman with no prior record, he had likely never felt that strain on his wrists. He glanced in my direction as the marshals led him through the courtroom to their holdover cell. I was numb and felt nothing.

In December 2010, Steve and I and his mother and sister journeyed to Colorado to visit Steve's son for the Christmas holiday. It was my first Christmas away from home and family. After a pleasant flight to Denver, we rented a car and drove through the mountains of Breckenridge, Snowmass, and Vail to the beautiful canyons outside Glenwood Springs, Colorado.

ALLISON—December 26, 2010: I'm in Colorado for Christmas. The trip has really been good. I was nervous, didn't know what to expect and worried about being away from home at Christmas but it has been fun and gone smoothly. Steve makes me so happy and I think that's why it was ok being away from home because

Steve kind of is "my home." When I talked to dad yesterday, he got choked up. I think he was kind of lonely and then he seemed worried about me and me not having "a family." But I love my life. I guess I could worry about my "later years" but I don't.

It is December; the year is marching to a close. Carolyn, Dad, Ellie, and I are seated at Carolyn's dining room table. We are enjoying lunch together before Dad and Becki journey off for Naples, Florida, for several months. Ellie, now age four, says to me, "Ali, that's your daddy," grinning and pointing at my father. I respond, "Yes, Ellie, it is, and he is your mommy's daddy too." Ellie replies, "Your mommy died." She doesn't know death, but she seems to comprehend that this statement brings sadness, so in a cheery demeanor, she announces, "But that's OK because you still have your daddy!" I glance at my father and tears have formed in his twinkling eyes. Ellie continues by telling us that she sees Grandma Jane in her bedroom (the theme from the Twilight Zone is now running through my head), but she clarifies by explaining that she has a photograph of Grandma Jane at her bedside.

In this dream, my mother and her sisters (Aunt Carol and Aunt Clodie) are lounging on the sofa in matching nightgowns. They are in their fifties and look like triplets. Aunt Carol sewed the flannel nightwear. The soft fabric is dotted with small pink flowers and dark green vines. They are looking at something in my mother's lap and laughing. I am watching them giggle but sense that I am not supposed to be there, that it is a private joke. The sofa is pointed in the wrong direction, so the room looks awkward. I feel as though I am interrupting, but they don't seem to notice me. How can they not see me standing here? Their heads tilt back, their mouths open wide; they are so alike when they laugh. What is so funny? I want to know. There is so much I still want to know.

2011

(I am forty-four)

The year commences with inspiration and a friend poses the question to me, "Why not write the book?" I am inspired by Diana and Emily, because they have begun a blog and website, finally making a commitment to sell their artwork and creative ideas. And so I begin. I rummage through all of my old journals and peruse my mother's. At times, I am weeping at my computer and must stop padding my fingers to the keys. Can I tiptoe through this journey unscathed? What if I don't succeed? What if this is a terrible mistake? I am inflated with excitement but overwhelmed with doubt. Perhaps this is all part of the "process." When I run, I am often flooded with memories, excerpts I must include. I write and delete. I pen more ideas and discard others. By summer, I submit the first draft to my sisters and Steve. I rework, add, remove, evolve, and yet, I can't decide where this path is headed.

In October, on a cloudless day, I visit her grave. It is Halloween, so a trip to the cemetery seems surreal but odd. As I stand next to her headstone, I tell my mother about the manuscript. I explain that I have written a book to honor her, her memory and struggle. I hope that she is proud and will help guide me through the rest of this voyage. Grave diggers are nearby. Has someone else lost their mother? The leaves rustle and a cool breeze whips through my hair. Perhaps a cemetery on October 31 is not where I wish to commune.

On December 23, Steve and I return to Colorado for another Christmas with his son. We have already spent a fun-filled weekend celebrating the holiday with my family, but again I am nervous to be away from home and what I know Christmas to be. Tradition. My mother instilled a keen sense of tradition in me, so much so that I could become caught up in it, trapped by tradition. If holidays, particularly Christmas, did not live up to my expectations, I felt let down and disappointed. When I was married, this was often the case. The weekend in Colorado became the alter ego to my traditional Christmas. And yet, without the confines of "tradition," I found a sense of peace within myself.

A morning run on a cool 25-degree day, eyeing the mountains of Glenwood Canyon and peering at the Colorado River, transformed my Christmas Eve. I woke on Christmas morning to a text from Carolyn . . . "Merry Christmas! Not a creature is stirring in this house!" I lay in the strange bed, listening to a neighbor's wind chimes and reminiscing about Christmases past. A tradition I had forgotten . . . Dad would line our driveway with small brown paper bags filled with sand and a tea light. As stars blanketed the night sky, the tea lights were lit, converting our driveway into a "runway" for Santa. I am hundreds of miles and a lifetime away from that ritual, but I smile and appreciate that it is part of my past.

Steve and I and his son visit the Glenwood Canyon Hot Springs and swim in steamy, soothing bath water with dozens of other vacationers. I've never experienced this on Christmas Day! I connect by phone with my sisters, nieces and father. I gaze at the snow-covered mountains and feel content. Perhaps what my mother taught me is that no matter where you are, you are responsible for your own happiness. Your circumstances, health, or situation may not be ideal, but your life is what you make of it. I have found you can create your own happiness, just by expanding your idea of what tradition looks like. So, I begin to focus on the small wonders of the holiday . . . saying "Merry Christmas" to strangers, stopping in a boutique offering free, warm snicker-doodle cookies, sipping a pint of ale in the local pub on Christmas Eve. Trapped in tradition, I would not have had these experiences, and perhaps they have led me to appreciate my family and home even more.

2012

(I am forty-five)

I awake from this dream to the bird's aria just outside my window . . . "whippoorwill . . . whippoorwill" . . . the air is fresh and crisp; spring has arrived. But perhaps I have not broken from sleep, because my mother is here. She is lying near the end of my bed and teaching me about the whippoorwill, the bird whose name derives from the sound it makes. My mother loved birds, their freedom of movement, their grace. Slowly, my eyes unfold and I am lying in my bed. It is 2012, she isn't here . . . but the whippoorwill is perched on a limb just beyond the glass.

I hope you have enjoyed this journey as much as I have. To other motherless daughters, I would offer that though time does not heal, it does help. I could not have imagined writing about these experiences, in 1999 or 2000, After. But through the years, I have discovered peace. That is not to say that I don't miss my mother, but she has left me with a gift that some never receive. I watched her live through pain and suffering yet maintain joy in her heart. She remained optimistic and loving despite the worst of circumstances. For myself, I have waded through grief and the fallout from death and managed to prosper, find happiness, and cherish the childhood I was given. If nothing else, I hope our story inspires you to begin a journal, for yourself, your child or a loved one to cherish after you have gone. To open each diary and view my mother's handwriting and candid words bring a comfort that cannot be described.

And though she is not porcelain, I now have an angel by my side.

Afterword

As I was completing the first draft of my manuscript, my sister Carolyn went rummaging in her attic and stumbled upon a weathered blue journal. The binding is frayed, the pages yellowed with time, and the back cover dangles loosely by threads of parchment. When the cover is carefully unfolded, the printed words "This is My Personal DIARY" appear. Underneath those words, with delicate hand, the owner has written in pencil . . . "Miss Jane Rolston, Franklin Ill 1946"

(My mother is ten)

JANE—January 3, 1946: We went to school, came home for dinner and went back to school. After school we skated on the ice at the church. When we got home we practiced our music. We had supper then after supper we played a little while, then we went to bed.

JANE—January 13, 1946: We went to Sunday school and church. Then we had dinner. We played at home a while then we went to the store and built a bird house. When we got home we listened to the radio till supper time.

JANE—January 16, 1946: We went to school. I went to band practice then ate lunch at school. After school we came home and helped Mother and practiced our music. After supper I took my music lesson.

JANE—February 9, 1946: Today is my birthday. We got up about 8:00. We helped Mother and played until dinner. I had a birthday party from 2:00 to 5:30. We play bunko and memory games. We had peanuts, ice cream and cake. Then we went outside and played awhile. We had supper and made valentines until time to go to bed.

JANE—February 14, 1946: We went to school. Before school was out we had ice cream and passed out the Valentines. After school we played and got the house cleaned up. After supper Mother and Daddy hid little red hearts and we hunted for them. We had a Valentine box. Then Daddy passed out the valentines to us kids from them.

They gave us two, one was a popcorn ball and the other was some candy. Then we played another game. Then we went to bed.

JANE—April 7, 1946: We went to Sunday school and church. After dinner we rode the bicycle. Then we went to the timber and picked flowers. It rained when we got home so we played in the play house. After supper we read and went to bed.

As spring arrived, my mother described how she and her sisters would "jump the rope" after school. It appears the four siblings shared a single bicycle. Their grandparents had a pony, and riding him always promised to be a joyous event. There are also entries that my mother "read the funny papers" (comics) and the family went to "the" restaurant on rare occasions. In the summer, they woke each morning and "got our work done," sewed doll clothes, played "pitch and catch," and caught lightning bugs in the evenings. I noticed that on many days my mother and her siblings played Flinch. When I read the journal, I had never heard of the card game and therefore I conducted a Google search to learn what I could about their evening activity. Google describes it as a card game, played with a custom deck, invented in 1901 by A. J. Patterson.

It appears that as a young girl, my mother's journal writing was much like mine. We recited the days' activities, regardless of how mundane and repetitive the entries seemed. My mother's handwriting appears much as it did when, years later she wrote letters to me at summer camp or college. I often wonder when it is in our lives that we begin to analyze, reflect, and, for some, put into words, our feelings and perceptions about those daily activities; when the journal becomes less a calendar of events and more a collection of thoughts, introspection, and ideation.

I meditate on this "final" journal and daydream of what my mother's young life was like, when she had not a care in the world. Her whole life lay ahead, full of possibilities, triumphs, and, regretfully, many struggles. And though this diary offers little of how my mother perceived the world around her, I take comfort in knowing that the grace, courage, and strength with which she battled multiple sclerosis were traits beginning to develop in the ten-year-old who began recording her life in 1946.

Acknowledgements

I would like to thank my sisters and father for their loving support and for allowing me to open our family to others in such an intimate fashion. My sisters and nieces have been my cheerleaders in more ways than one, and I greatly appreciate the time they took to read my manuscript, though apparently, often through tears. Diana designed the cover for this book and her artistry is a gift of which I am constantly in awe. I am also so grateful for my loving partner, Steve, who told me to "go for it" and never seemed to doubt that something wonderful could come from all of this writing. Many thanks go to my dear friend, Denise, who eagerly offered to read the manuscript early on in the process. I felt my first wave of confidence after Steve and Denise praised what I had written, as they never met my mother and were still moved by her story. I would also like to thank my cousin, Lisa, and friends, Sue, Sherry and Judy, who read every page and offered insightful feedback. And most of all, thank you Mom.

To find your local MS chapter, for information or to make a donation, go to www.nmss.org